Scientists
and
Amateurs

King Charles II

PLATE 1

(From *The Signatures in the First Journal Book and the Charter Book of the Royal Society*, London, 1912, by courtesy of the Royal Society)

SCIENTISTS
AND
AMATEURS

A History of the Royal Society

D O R O T H Y   S T I M S O N

GREENWOOD PRESS, PUBLISHERS
NEW YORK   1968

*To my students
in History 111 (41)
at Goucher College
1922–1947*

PREFACE

THE STORY of a man's life has great interest especially if that man has been connected with important affairs, whether in philosophy or statesmanship, discovery or invention. Similarly, the story of an organization or institution which is the product of ideas and labors of many men for generations can hardly fail to be of interest as well as of importance. For this reason the writer presents this account of the origins and development through the centuries of the leading scientific society in the English-speaking world today. Those who have the time and the opportunity to look through the Royal Society's own *Record* or to refer to its treasurer's recent careful study of its administration for nearly three centuries may not need this book. But copies of neither book are readily available to an American public because of cost or scarcity, nor is either one planned for the general reader who knows little or nothing of the Royal Society at the outset. It is hoped, therefore, that this history may not only interest the general reader in the life-story of a great and influential institution, but that it may also indicate to him many possibilities for further reading and exploration in the field of the history of science and of scientific ideas.

The book itself is the outgrowth of various studies in the history of scientific activity in seventeenth century England pursued by the writer since 1930. These studies were made possible in the first instance by the beneficence of the John Simon Guggenheim Memorial Foundation of

vii

which the writer was a fellow in 1930-31, and in the second instance by the courtesy of the officers of the Royal Society in allowing reproduction of their treasured possessions, and by the helpfulness of the librarian and his staff during the weeks the writer was privileged to use that Library. She has also made much use of the publications of others who have preceded or followed her there among the Society's archives.

In recent years increased study and recognition have been given to various aspects of the Society's interrelationships with general intellectual activities especially during the first two hundred years of its history. In chapter references the writer has expressed her indebtedness to such studies and their authors, and hopes that her own rendering of the Society's history may stimulate new accounts of the subject in more detail than has been possible within the limited scope of her own work. Especially there is room for an account of the Society's major activities in the past hundred years when it participated more and more in the great scientific advances of the age. Such an account lies outside the scope of this introduction to the Society's history, by reason of the highly specialized character of the subject matter and its technical terminology.

The author wishes to express her deep appreciation of the generous loan made to her by Professor John F. Fulton of Yale University, of rare books from his private library. She is greatly indebted to the librarians in many places who have helped her locate needed material, particularly to those in the library of Goucher College, the Enoch Pratt Public Library, the Peabody Library and the Welch Library, all of Baltimore; to those in the libraries of Columbia University and the New York Public Library; and to those in the Historical Library of the Yale School of Medicine at New Haven and in the Public Library of Westerly, Rhode Island.

The writer is under deep obligation to the authorities of Goucher College who acceded graciously to her request for temporary relief from her academic duties, giving her the opportunity to complete this book, and to the friends and relatives who have borne with her struggles, helped with suggestions and criticisms and generally smoothed her path. Especially is she indebted to Miss Edith Bruce Paterson of Baltimore, who has on occasion used her scanty leisure to run down an elusive fact or has suggested some pertinent discovery from her own omnivorous reading. Finally, she is grateful for the criticism and the encouragement given her by her publisher. At the same time she takes upon herself full responsibility for whatever may be found amiss in this book, thankful that her friendly critics have saved her from many more mistakes.

D.S.

November 28, 1947.

CONTENTS

Preface   vii

Chapters

  1 Contrasts in Centuries   3
  2 The Dreamers   8
  3 The Virtuosi   26
  4 The Founding of the Royal Society   46
  5 Early Opposition   70
  6 The Critical Years   97
  7 Stability   116
  8 Targets for Satire   133
  9 Contacts Overseas   147
 10 Conservatism   161
 11 Expansion versus Tradition   179
 12 Unhappy Years   197
 13 New Growth   220
 14 The Royal Society in Recent Years   236

Bibliography and Sources   251

Index   263

ILLUSTRATIONS

Plates

1	King Charles II	FRONTISPIECE
2	John Evelyn	*facing page* 16
3	Sir Thomas Gresham	17
4	Gresham College	17
5	"How any man may blow up the greatest oak"	48
6	Doctor John Wilkins	48
7	First Page of the Journal Book	49
8	The Mace	80
9	Henry Oldenburg	81
10	Dr. Wilkins' Report on Experiment	112
11	Frontispiece of Sprat's *History*	113
12	The Honorable Robert Boyle	144
13	The Treasurer's Chest	145
14	Sir Isaac Newton	176
15	The Crane Court House	177
16	The Meeting Room, Somerset House	177
17	Charles II by Lely	208
18	The Library, Burlington House, 1910	209
19	The Meeting Room, Burlington House, 1912	240
20	The Meeting Room, Burlington House, 1939	241

Scientists
and
Amateurs

1

CONTRASTS IN CENTURIES

IF BY MAGIC a man of the twentieth century were whisked back three hundred and fifty years to the London of Queen Elizabeth's day, he would feel strange and out of place, in spite of the excitement over the New World, the defeat of the Spanish Armada, the rapid development of trade and the enjoyment of seeing Shakespeare's plays as they were first presented.

The Times of Queen Elizabeth and of Cromwell

These people, for instance, still believed the earth to be the center of the universe, around which whirled the sun, the moon and the seven planets in their circular paths as Aristotle ages before had laid down and Claudius Ptolemy confirmed. To be sure there were rumors that some Pole named Copernicus fifty years before had written that the earth was but one of the planets and that the sun and not the earth was the center of the universe; but hardly anyone paid attention to that notion. There were also rumors of a perspective glass that brought far objects close to hand. Two Englishmen, Leonard and Thomas Digges, were said to have devised it, and to have claimed that the heavens, far from being fixed and crystalline as everyone knew they were, were myriad in number and stretched out into infinite space. Few cared about such talk even though that wandering Italian monk, Giordano Bruno, had talked much about infinite space and even the outrageous possibility of other worlds existing, when he had stayed at Oxford and in London for three years shortly before the sinking of the Spanish Armada. To most men such things were foolishness, for had not their forefathers and all the learned men for centuries past upheld the authority of the great Aristotle, the Master of those who know. And he had said, as the Bible did also, that the heavens were above and the earth beneath and all creation revolved around man, while the earth was man's footstool. Anyone could see with his own eyes that the sun rose in the east and set in the west and could feel that the earth was steady under his feet.

But let magic work again and bring the twentieth-century man fifty years on to the middle of the seventeenth century, how would he feel? My guess is, very much more at home. True, the clothes people wore still would be strange. Even London itself would seem like a small town with outlying villages and country places. But the very air would seem to have changed, to have come alive and to sparkle with discoveries and inventions startling in themselves and prophetic of more marvels to come. The future looked more promising than the past and why not? For surely, as Francis Bacon had expressed it, if children stood on their fathers' shoulders they would see further than their fathers did, and was that not what scholars then were doing, learning from the past and standing on that knowledge looking forward? Maybe Aristotle would have said things differently if he had known what they now knew about the world about them. For instance, what would Aristotle have said had he known of the New World, of gunpowder, or of the printing press? More and more people were listening to daring innovators, though there were plenty still who held firmly to the ancient learning, distrusting the modern because it was modern.

This change in the climate of ideas affected other matters beside learning. The twentieth-century man would have felt more at home with the problems of the Stuart kings and of Cromwell than in the England under Queen Elizabeth; for even as now, governments were unsteady, kings were on trial, wars raged, dictatorships threatened, and people were driven out of their homelands to seek refuge in far countries. Men's personal liberties were at stake then as now, though in different ways. Censorship confronted the daring writer and both the unlucky author and his printer might find themselves imprisoned in the Tower of London, or fastened in the pillory, or minus their ears. Milton was fighting for the freedom of the press while others were fighting for their own and others' right to believe about religion as their own consciences thought best, and to have church services conducted according to those beliefs. It was a time of deep-felt conviction as well as of violent change.

It was also an age of experiment and of invention, of great scientists and of great discoveries, of a growing realization of the importance of cooperation in scientific activity and of a desire to know what others were doing and of sharing with them the excitement of one's own investigations. Social distinctions between nobleman and commoner became of less importance when the proper method of growing potatoes was being discussed or what happened when clothes were dyed or meat spoiled. Where did maggots come from anyway? The men of Cromwell's time in the 1650's had seen so many wonders,—a king beheaded, the mightiest nobles fallen, the king's armies defeated by God-fearing common folk, the Dutch driven back even though they had sailed threateningly up the

English rivers, and in addition friends and relatives finding homes for themselves in a New World of even greater marvel than any their ancestors had dreamed of. What strange thing was impossible now? Might not men be able to travel underwater? Suppose there were people on the moon; could not someone find a way to go there and see? How about horseless carriages and machines that might fly in the air?

Thus in the fifty years between Queen Elizabeth's old age in 1600 and the beheading of Charles I in 1649, notable changes had come over English thought. Many forces were at work bringing these about beside the great struggle of Parliament against the divine right of kings. In the church the authority of the bishops was contested and in the universities that of Aristotle, the Greek philosopher, and of Galen, the ancient Roman physician. The trading companies favored by Queen Elizabeth had grown and expanded, bringing more wealth to more people, and with that wealth more leisure and time to consider new ideas. More people were reading, and more books were available in English, in addition to those in the Latin of the scholars.

Seamen and traders returned from far voyages bringing ostrich eggs and humming-birds' nests, as well as powder from the fabulous unicorn's horn. Men sampled the tobacco that Sir Walter Raleigh had brought back with him from the New World. They drank hot chocolate, wondering whether it was really true that it would make them passionate. They welcomed coffee so gladly that before long the coffee-houses (where it could be bought) became the social and political centers of the town where men could meet their friends, exchange views, and learn the news of the day. There they could ask each other if it could be true that the blood pumped by the heart circulated through the body, as that great doctor, William Harvey, had written in 1628. Or was it true that the Roman Church had thought that strange theory about the universe held by Copernicus important enough to condemn it as heretical and to punish Galileo for teaching it? Yet wasn't Galileo that Florentine professor whose telescope had revealed that the planet Jupiter had moons encircling it and that even the sun had spots on it despite Aristotle's claim of the perfection of the heavens? Their curiosity aroused by what they had heard and seen, some of these Londoners wanted to learn more, undisturbed and uninterrupted by the news of the day and by arguments over public affairs.

Organized Amateurs

Some ten or so of these particularly inquiring young men by 1645 had formed a kind of luncheon club, agreeing to meet once a week to discuss and experiment together, in further pursuit of their common interest, this "new philosophy" that we know today as experimental science. They agreed to pay each a shilling * a meeting to cover expenses and they agreed to refrain from any discussion of the current news and questions of the day. Science would be their sole topic.

A similar society was soon founded in Oxford when some of these Londoners moved there with appointments from the parliamentary authorities to replace the royalists ejected after the king's defeat. Then with the Restoration of the Stuart rulers in 1660, these parliamentary appointees were ejected in their turn and royalists reappointed. Returning to London the Oxford men rejoined their former associates and both together decided to organize more formally, if possible under the patronage of Charles II himself. This was done, and thus the Royal Society was established in 1662.

* A shilling in 1645 may have had a purchasing value of as much as eight or ten times the twenty cents it represents now.

5

The Royal Society

Today, three centuries later, the Royal Society flourishes,—no longer a small luncheon club, but now the leading scientific society in the English-speaking world. By the terms of the charter granted the Society by Charles II, its members and their successors "whose studies are to be applied to further promoting by the authority of experiments the sciences of natural things and of useful arts, to the glory of God the Creator, and the advantage of the human race," were to be known as the Royal Society of London for promoting Natural Knowledge.

Membership in it has now become the crowning glory for scientific achievement, welcomed by foreigners as well as by the British. Its approval means recognition for a scientist, its verdict on scientific matters is sought by individuals and by the government alike, its gifts of medals are highly prized, and its support for further research is eagerly sought.

How did it happen that a society of notable men in the London of the seventeenth century should so have transformed itself that by the twentieth century the organization had become a guide and leader in scientific progress? As often happens with living organisms, the changes were not continuously directed toward one goal, nor was that goal envisioned by the men directing the Royal Society's fortunes. The Society proved that it had an enduring vitality within itself. Thus it eventually overcame its handicaps, survived its periods of stress and gradually emerged into its present position of power and prestige.

Embedded in its history is many an interesting story concerning its difficulties and struggles. At least three times there was a good chance that it might not survive,—in the critical years before Newton became its president, in the mid-eighteenth century when it wasted its strength over trivialities, and in the early nineteenth century when its critics claimed it had lapsed into its second childhood.

An account of these troubles must be set against the background of the Society's environment for their better understanding.

As time passes, old happenings are seen in different lights, and new interpretations give fresh meaning to old events. Helped by the perspective of history, later generations may uncover facts long forgotten or ignored that give a different meaning to an age-old situation and a clearer appreciation of what actually happened. Sometimes, too, an earlier century seems to resemble closely the present age. Because of that resemblance, men of today may gain greater understanding and appreciation of a past era than would its immediate successors.

Thus the twentieth century in some ways has much in common with the seventeenth; for both are insecure, with the old order dying and the new order not fully arrived. New devices in government and war, insistent questioning of religion, education and philosophy, upheavals among peoples from disaster and disease as well as from war, both civil and foreign, startling novelties in science and invention,—all these may be found in both centuries. Perhaps as the reader living in the twentieth century turns his imagination and his thought to the origins of one of the great institutions of our own day and follows its development down through the intervening centuries, he may better appreciate the age of science in which he is living, and may realize that not all his present problems are new ones.

2

THE DREAMERS

EVENTS, like thunderstorms, do not "just happen." They have a long preparation behind them, often not recognized as such until ages later. An important part of this preparation is a mental one. Many people have to be thinking, writing, discussing an idea and considering its various ramifications and possibilities before that idea takes shape in some new institution or new device. Whether that new institution or device is welcomed and developed or whether it dies immediately depends in part upon the mental attitude of the general public at the time. Does it meet a long felt need? Does it have practical value? Or is it merely startling in its novelty and shocking in its disregard for long-established customs and practices? Consequently, those who dream dreams which they express even in fantastic form are often important aids in bringing to pass a great change.

Some of those who helped to prepare the way for the Royal Society and the development of modern science were dreamers who lived in the time of Queen Elizabeth and of her successor, James I. Others were among the actual founders of the Society in the middle of the seventeenth century. In criticizing the educational procedures of their day—a favorite subject of all ages—some dreamers, men of affairs as well as of letters, were led on in their thought to consider the life about them and the part played in it by what we now call science and which they called natural philosophy. They held that neither the two universities, Oxford and Cambridge, nor the system of apprenticeship for poor lads, prepared young men adequately for their later life either in the king's councils or in the world of trade and business. Much time was being wasted. Therefore they suggested various changes for the schools and the universities.

Sir Humphrey Gilbert

One of these dreamers was Sir Walter Raleigh's half-brother, Sir Humphrey Gilbert. Early in Queen Elizabeth's reign he proposed a plan for an academy for the youth of London, especially for her majesty's wards and for the sons of the nobility and the upper classes. He considered the universities of his time a waste of a boy's time except for "learning"—no other gentlemanlike qualities were there attained and there were too many evil examples. Accordingly, in his academy the professors should teach "matters of action meet for present practice both of peace and warre" and their pupils should at least learn their own language and should have martial exercises. His emphasis upon learning in English is notable and unusual; for in those days the language of schools, as of all scholarship, was Latin. But Sir Humphrey wrote: "In what language soever learning is attained, the appliance to use is principally in the vulgar speech as in preaching, in parliament, in council, in commissions and other offices of common weal."

Then too, Sir Humphrey's professors were not only to lecture on the usual university subjects of that period, but they were also to put their teaching to the practical test. They were to study nature itself and search out its secrets, making annual report to the crown in clear English on their experiments and their results. The doctor of physick (medicine) for example, was to lecture on physick and on chirurgerie (surgery) on alternate days in English, always giving the reasons for every step in his procedure, and showing the ingredients in his medicines, and their respective merits. Sir Humphrey added that there were few if any good surgeons then "by reason that chirurgerie is not now to be learned in any other place than in a barber's shop." This doctor of physick should also have a garden for his herbs and a special fund for his expenses.

Sir Humphrey Gilbert's academy never was founded; but the plan he gave in detail shows how some at least were criticizing education for not sufficiently emphasizing possible practical values. By implication it also shows how far apart was the learning of the schools from everyday life, and how secret and private was a scholar's knowledge.

Francis Bacon

Much more important and more influential were the ideas of another of Queen Elizabeth's courtiers, Sir Francis Bacon, later Lord Chancellor under James I. A scholar, sometimes considered the last of the encyclopedic schoolmen of the middle ages, he was deeply concerned both for the advancement of learning for its own sake and for the practical results that would ensue. Although he scorned or ignored the new learning of his day, the ideas of Copernicus, of Gilbert and of Galileo, he recognized the need for a different method of approach from that of ancient times, if knowledge were to grow and develop as he thought it should. Conspicuous because of his high place and stimulating because of his ideas, Bacon was particularly influential in that he wrote in English with an eloquence remarkable even to this day.

For centuries before him learned men had been using the old well-worn form of reasoning known as syllogistic or deductive reasoning. Thus they worked out their ideas logically in a pattern moving from major principles or axioms step by step to conclusions. The simplest and most familiar syllogism is the ancient one: All men are mortal, Socrates is a man; therefore he is mortal. If you accept the first or major statement as true, and the second or minor one also, then the conclusion is logically inescapable. The Greek philosophers, especially Aristotle, had formulated the laws of reasoning and the schoolmen of the middle ages had crystallized the pattern as they understood it. Therefore it had the weight of authority and of centuries of use behind it.

This syllogistic reasoning by deduction worked well for the re-statement and proof of what was already known; but it was not particularly fruitful, as Bacon pointed out, for the discovery of new knowledge. Far better, according to him, was it to assemble facts by observation and experiment, consider their similarities and their dissimilarities, and then on the basis of the evidence before one's eyes, to theorize. Such theories, if well reasoned and supported, should have predictive value and would lead on to further discoveries, and so truth would grow and knowledge expand. The ancient Greeks and Romans, the great leaders of the Church, had done well in their times; but knowledge was not limited to what they knew nor was it necessarily correct because they said so in the ancient books that scholars still were supposed to study. Men should test and try for themselves to see if an idea would work. And the story goes that Bacon came to his death from a chill he caught when on a drive he stopped to stuff a chicken with snow "to try whether it would preserve flesh from putrefaction, as salt does." He reported that the experiment "succeeded excellently well"; but his own death followed in a few days from this illness.

Bacon wrote many books, three of them of especial importance to the "new learning." In one, the *Novum Or-*

ganum, (the *New Logic*) he explained the importance of inductive reasoning, of proceeding from facts and details to generalizations or principles. In this he answered Aristotle's *Organon,* the great book on logic and syllogistic reasoning that had dominated men's minds for more than fifteen centuries. In the *Advancement of Learning* Bacon charted the fields of knowledge as he knew them, pointing out great regions awaiting exploration and also indicating some of the difficulties men must be prepared to meet in making those explorations. Finally in 1626, a few months after his death, his unfinished *New Atlantis* was published, a picture of an imaginary country where people lived under the government and the institutions Bacon thought wisest. The most important one of these he called the House of Salomon, which today we would recognize as an institute for research on the grand scale.

In this House and around it he would provide all the equipment a scientist could dream of—laboratories for the study of heat and light and cold, and for the testing of medicines and of minerals, instruments for observing and recording all the changes of the weather, gardens, pools, zoos, and vineyards, houses for the study of perfumes as well as of engines and other crafts, caves and high towers for subterranean and atmospheric studies, astronomical instruments,—in short every conceivable aid for observation and experiment in natural phenomena to uncover their possible utility for mankind.

The staff assembled at Salomon's House were to be thirty-six in number, together with their assistants. These "Fellows" were divided in groups, each group with its special part of the general undertaking. Some were to visit foreign countries for years at a time, "Merchants of Light" he called them, to collect observations of all sorts for the service of the fellows at the House itself. Other groups were to read the literature of the ages and to abstract from it useful experiments already known. Still others were to investigate the mechanical arts and crafts for the same reason. Nearly half the fellows were to spend their days trying new experiments, compiling the materials reported on, searching for new uses and demonstrations and seeking ever to penetrate nature more deeply. Finally, three fellows whom Bacon named the Interpreters of Nature were to draw forth from all this work conclusions useful for man's life and knowledge, and from them to formulate greater observations, axioms and principles.

Particularly in his House of Salomon Bacon forecast the major characteristics of modern scientific development; the experimental method, specialization, cooperative activity, and reliance upon equipment and books as all-inclusive as possible with ample funds to subsidize fulltime work. His fellows were to give their entire time to this research, supported by the House. And their work was directed both to present usefulness and to future possibilities. No such all-embracing institute exists or could exist; but by it Bacon illustrated the "closer and purer League" between the experimental and the rational faculties which had not then before been attempted and from which he hoped much. Facts even from experiment would have little meaning unless they were correlated and properly interpreted, and progress could best come where this was done cooperatively and systematically by men freed from all other cares.

The *New Atlantis* with its dream of Salomon's House aroused great interest. Ten different editions of the book were issued by 1670, one of these in September, 1660, just after the restoration of Charles II to the throne. That Bacon's schemes were much in the minds of the founders of the Royal Society in those years is proved not only by the many references in their writings to the Baconian or "new" philosophy, experimental science, but by the place Bacon has as "instauratio artium"—"restorer of the arts"— in the frontispiece Evelyn designed and Sprat used for his *History of the Royal Society* in 1667. On one side of the pedestal with the King's bust on it sits the figure of the Society's president, on the other sits Bacon. (See Plate 10.) Thus Sprat and the Fellows of the Society who helped him write his *History,* in addition to sponsoring it, bore witness that they derived their chief inspiration from the author of the *Novum Organum,* the *Advancement of Learning* and the *New Atlantis.*

Comenius and Hartlib

Inspiration came also from other sources, some of these European. Another great thinker deeply concerned about the education of children and about learning in general was the Czech, Comenius, who visited England in 1641. To him language was "the gateway to knowledge, and his aim was to simplify and shorten by a kind of royal road to learning, all studies, arts and sciences." Languages should be learned in relation to real objects, not through the disputations of the schoolmen. He evolved an entire system of education to be crowned by a great university of all knowledge, which he accordingly called a "pansophic" university.

Scholars in England learning about his ideas urged Comenius to come to London, which he finally did. His hope was with the aid of his European-born friends in London to win support for his university from the great English nobles and even from Parliament itself. But the times were out of joint. The struggle between king and parliament was breaking into civil warfare, and neither the nobles nor the king were interested at the moment in his pansophism. Comenius returned to the continent after a few months' stay, a greatly disappointed man. But his scheme of a pansophic university was another ingredient in the idea of a systematic study of nature in all its forms as part of the advance of learning, for some of the people he had met in England were among the science-lovers soon to band themselves together into a club to further the "new philosophy" that was a part of his plan.

Samuel Hartlib, one of the European-born friends of Comenius in London, is especially worth noting both as

14

a dreamer himself and as an important link in the chain of connections between science-lovers in days when there were no newspapers, no telegraph, no radio to announce new discoveries, new books and new workers. The dissemination of such intelligence—as news of all sorts was called in those days—is especially important for scientists whose work knows no political boundaries. The men who served as intelligencers in the seventeenth century were as indispensable then as newspapers and journals are now.

Hartlib was perhaps the best-known of these intelligencers in the reign of Charles I. "Everybody knew him," one biographer wrote, and he served as a clearing-house for all kinds of European as well as English news. Half English and half Polish-German and born in Elbing near Danzig, he had been at Cambridge in the 1620s and had remained in England as a merchant after 1628, keeping up correspondence and connection with his European friends while at the same time living in the thick of London affairs. A public-spirited man especially interested in education, it was he who had succeeded in getting Comenius to cross the Channel into England, and as his sponsor had done what he could, writing to friends in his behalf, introducing him and arranging appointments with influential people, but all in vain. Another twenty years had to pass before the advance of the new learning could proceed under royal patronage.

Samuel Hartlib, however, had his own dream which he published in 1641. In his *Description of the Famous Kingdom of Macaria* there would be "a common centre for assisting and promoting all undertakings in the support of which mankind was interested." Included was a college of husbandry, of farming. And for the advancement of universal learning he planned a college which he called "Antlantis." For this college he sought advice and financial help from other science-lovers, especially from Robert Boyle, soon to become one of the greatest and best-know among them.

Hartlib himself apparently was not one of the "expe

mentalists," though one of his sons was and he had many friends in the group. In 1654 Hartlib wrote in a letter to Boyle: "As for us, poor earth-worms, we are crawling in my house about our quondam back-kitchen, whereof my son hath made a goodly laboratory; yea, such a one, as men (who have had the favour and privilege to see, or to be admitted into it) affirm, they have never seen the like, for its several advantages and commodiousnesses." Later he added that one of the nobles he knew had remarked that nowhere in his travels had he met "so much of theoretical solidity and practical dexterity, both together, as he finds in my chemical son." But Hartlib's own name does not appear among those first science-lovers who came together weekly, and he had died the year the Royal Society was chartered.[1]

Where Bacon's purpose was to search out "the knowledge of causes and secret motions of things," Hartlib was earnest to have his college, his Antlantis, "demonstrate any experiment for the health or wealth of other men," so that men may live "in great plenty, prosperity, health, peace and happiness." Both men saw great need for the histories of the trades men used, Bacon for the advancement of learning, Hartlib and some of his friends for the immediate betterment of society. Urged on by Hartlib, one of these friends, William Petty, wrote *The Advice of W. P. to Mr. S. Hartlib for the Advancement of Some Particular Parts of Learning* (1648).

William Petty

Petty, only twenty-four at this time, the son of a poor clothier and dyer, had already worked and studied much abroad (he had shipped as an apprentice before he was fourteen). He had made influential friends on the continent who helped develop his marked mechanical and lin-

[1] G. H. Turnbull. *Hartlib, Dury and Comenius: Gleanings from Hartlib's Papers.* (London, 1947) 11, 13, 297.

PLATE 2. John Evelyn, F.R.S., 1620-1706

(From *The Record of the Royal Society*, London, 1940, by courtesy of the Royal Society)

THOMAS GRESHAMVS EQVES AVRATVS
EXCAMBII REGII COLLEGIIQVE COGNOMINIS
CONDITOR

PLATE 3. Sir Thomas Gresham, 1519-1579

(From Ward's *Lives of the Professors of Gresham College*, 1740)

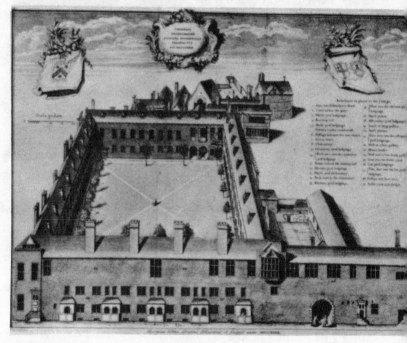

PLATE 4. Gresham College

(From Ward's *Lives of the Professors of Gresham College*, 1740)

guistic skills. During those years he had studied Greek and Latin as well as French and had learned anatomy besides geometry and navigation. Upon his father's death in 1646, he had returned to England to take up his father's trade with a special interest in all the mechanical processes involved in the industry. Three years later he received his medical degree and in two years more was professor of anatomy at Oxford. Soon thereafter he was appointed physician-general to the parliamentary army in Ireland where he displayed great administrative ability. He also undertook with marked success the mapping of the country and the survey of the forfeited estates of the Irish landowners. He is best known, however, for his "practical arithmetic," becoming one of the founders of political economy by his studies of taxation and similar subjects. A brilliant and accomplished man, Charles II knighted him in 1662.

This varied career was still ahead of Petty, however, when he wrote his book on education (1648). His interest in the Baconian philosophy was in its usefulness, and around that practical idea he shaped his educational program. He saw the need for a center, a rendezvous, where one could learn what had been done, what was in the doing and what was being planned,—a center for the general communication of designs and of mutual assistance. Both workers and equipment would be needed of course, and in addition there should be yearly reports and rewards. To train assistants, a school for children should be included where they could be taught to earn their living as well as to read and write. Among the mechanical arts to be taught them he suggested the turning of figures on a lathe, the making of mathematical instruments, engraving, the grinding of lenses, the making of musical instruments,—genteel manufactures that would be an ornament in prosperity, a stay in adversity.

Among the many details Petty gave for his scheme were suggestions for the kind of books needed. Among these should be a compilation of the ways of earning a living, with a history of the arts or manufactures and their tools all carefully worked out with illustrations. These histories of the various trades were not to be overloaded with detail but should give the various methods in use and their relative merits, and also their "economy,"—what seasons of the year were best, markets, the disposal or use of wastes, etc. Petty saw in his plan for the education of children great advantages, among them the shortening of the age-old seven years of apprenticeship to three years, which would leave four years for travel and for perfecting skills before the youths became of age.

These proposed histories of trade were not forgotten, even though Petty's scheme for a great center, like that of Comenius, did not materialize as he had detailed it. He joined the other science-lovers and became one of the charter members of the Royal Society. At the request of the Society he reported on the history of clothing, the history of dyeing and that of shipping. The Society asked others to write about varnish-making, engraving on copper, the making of bread, and the improvement of forests. Later, the Society formed a committee on the histories of trades and from these plans Sprat thought in 1667 that innumerable benefits would result for all practical arts. The advancement of learning Bacon advocated had its practical values as well as its theoretical ones, and Hartlib, Petty and their friends were many of them too able as business men not to emphasize these aspects in their own plans and activities.

But before the Royal Society was founded two other schemes were proposed by men later to be among its Fellows—John Evelyn and Abraham Cowley.

John Evelyn

John Evelyn (1620-1706) throughout his long life was a most useful amateur of science. Not a great experimenter nor a theorizer himself, he was full of ideas and encouragement for others, freely placing his wide knowl-

edge of men and affairs at the service of this new learning
and its enthusiasts.

After having been a student at the Middle Temple and
at Oxford (Balliol), with the outbreak of the Civil War
Evelyn found it wise because of his Royalist sympathies
to travel and live abroad. Both in Italy and in France, especially in Paris, he gained a wide acquaintance among the
intellectuals of Europe and among the Royalist exiles of
the Court. When Cromwell was firmly established in
power, he returned to England to live quietly on his
country estate, Sayes Court, until the Restoration. Thereafter Evelyn was much in London and was warmly welcomed at Court. Charles II appointed him commissioner
for various public services, such as the oversight of the
sick, wounded and prisoners of the Dutch War, and as a
member of the Council of Foreign Plantations, while under James II in 1685 he was commissioner of the Privy
Seal. For many years also until 1703 he was treasurer of
Greenwich Hospital for the Navy's wounded and pen-
sioners.

All these responsibilities Evelyn carried out in a prudent,
sober fashion reflected in the diary he kept from his boy-
hood days until he died. (First published in 1818, this
diary has provided historians ever since with an invaluable
record of the age in which he lived.) A large-minded man
with wide political, social and horticultural interests,
though he loved solitude and the life of a scholar, Evelyn
led an active life because he believed in public service.
Somehow or other he found time to write or to translate
some twenty-five books, of which his *Sylva* (1664) on for-
est-trees is perhaps the best-known. He gave much thought
and care to the development of his gardens, also. One likes
to think how pleased he would be were he to know now
that those same gardens, carefully tended by his descendants through the centuries, had in 1886 been given by the
Evelyn of the day to the public for their enjoyment.

Evelyn's interest in the "new philosophy" was deep and
abiding. With the development of the Royal Society he

19

had its welfare at heart, furthering its aims in every way at the Court as well as in the City, in good times and in bad; and among its members were his closest friends.

To one of these friends, Robert Boyle, just before the Restoration and the founding of the new Society, Evelyn proposed a society of his own. Intermingled in his scheme for the advancement of natural knowledge were also his love for solitude, his deep interest in gardening and his sense of public duty. "Since we are not to hope for a mathematical college," he wrote to Boyle in 1659, "much less a Salomon's House, . . . why might not some gentlemen, whose geniuses are greatly suitable, and who desire nothing more than to give a good example, preserve science, and cultivate themselves, join together in a society and resolve upon some orders and economy, to be mutually observed, such as shall best become the end of their union . . ."

Evelyn proposed the purchase of an estate not above twenty-five miles from London, and the building of a central pavilion for the library, dining-room, drawing-room, kitchens and other serving rooms, with a court in front, a garden or recreation place, beautifully kept, behind and a chapel nearby. There should be six apartments or cells for the members of the society, each one to consist of a small bedroom, a living-room, a closet and a private garden. A laboratory with a repository (museum) for rarities or specimens, an aviary, a dovecote, an herb garden, a vegetable garden, an orchard, a conservatory or greenhouse and a stable, with lodgings for one or two servants besides, should also be provided. He then proposed to Boyle that he (Evelyn) and his wife would each take one of the apartments, that Boyle should take the third and that the other three would be reserved for the nominees of the other founder of the institution, who he suggested, should be Boyle himself. Evelyn offered to pay a large share of the expense of building and also to subsidize the main building, if need be for seven years.

The principal end of this institution he conceived of

"was the promotion of natural knowledge." To that end and to free members' time for work, no stranger should be easily admitted except on special days and after dinner. Each member for one month in the year might leave to visit London or a university for travel "in the public benefit." What Boyle thought of this plan is not recorded; apparently he was not interested, or else the Restoration modified Evelyn's own desires.

Abraham Cowley

Another Royalist like Evelyn but a more active one, Abraham Cowley (1618-1667) had had his education first as a king's scholar at Westminster School and then at Trinity College, Cambridge. As a Royalist he was ejected from his fellowship there, and after two years at Oxford, followed the queen in 1646 to France where he served as a diplomatic messenger and as a cipher-expert in connection with her correspondence with the king. In England ten years later he was arrested but released on bail. With the Restoration he regained his full freedom and in 1665 established himself on a country estate at Chertsey.

Throughout all these years Cowley's pen was busy with poems, satires and odes; at the request of his close friend, Sprat, he wrote the *Ode to the Royal Society* which prefaces Sprat's *History*. He too was one of the first Fellows, for as his proposal shows, he was greatly interested in the new learning of his day. Indeed Sprat credited Cowley's plan as "greatly hastening the contrivance" of the Royal Society's "platform."

Cowley's *Proposition for the Advancement of Experimental Philosophy* (1661) was for no such hermit-like existence as Evelyn had fancied. Cowley proposed a college where twenty philosophers or professors with sixteen young scholars as their aids should be provided with living quarters, servants, ample funds and all the equipment and books necessary for four purposes: "1, to weigh, examine and prove all things of nature delivered to us by former ages, to detect, explode and strike a censure through all false monies with which the world has been paid and cheated so long; 2, to recover the lost inventions of the ancients; 3, to improve present arts; 4, to discover others we yet have not; and besides to give the best education in the world gratis." For this last purpose Cowley proposed that these professors should teach two hundred pupils living in the college with them. He drew up a course of study by which he thought they might advance in knowledge and in language not only by reading those authors who treat of nature, but also at the same time by serving an apprenticeship in natural philosophy in the laboratories and gardens to see the objects written about and the processes described.

Like Bacon's "merchants of light," four of Cowley's professors should always be traveling beyond the seas, one in Europe, one in Asia, one in Africa, and one in America, to be gone for at least three years. They were to give a constant account of all things that belong to learning and especially to natural or experimental philosophy. Nor were they ever to report back to the college on anything which they had not thoroughly examined themselves. Cowley, in this as well as in other parts of his scheme, showed that he knew Bacon's plans well. Indeed, after enumerating the instruments and laboratory equipment he would provide for the college, Cowley wrote that he could suggest more but that his college was not designed after Bacon's Salomon's House ("which is a project for experiments that can never be experimented"). He was content with proposing a scheme within the bounds of financial support by private citizens.

In the preface to his book, Cowley pointed out the inadequacies of the existing university education, with its reliance "solely upon memory and wit," thus ignoring, except for some very slight aid to medicine and to mathematics, two other parts of learning: one, "the inquisition into God's creatures," the other, the application of this knowledge to practical living. The universities had an ample provision of books and tutors for reading and interpretation but none for observation and application, partly because of their cost, and partly "for that idle and pernicious opinion which had long possessed the world, that all things to be searched in nature had been already found and discovered by the ancients, and that it were a folly to travel about for that which others had before brought home to us. And the great importer of all truths they took to be Aristotle, as if . . . he could neither deceive nor be deceived, or as if there had been not only no lies in him, but all verities . . . No man can hope to make himself as rich by stealing out of others' trunks as he might by opening and digging of new mines." Obviously all knowledge was not known before, for only recently had America been discovered. Nor could man learn by the solitary and inactive contemplation of nature in his private study. In the past thousand years, according to Cowley, nothing had been added to society except guns and printing; but since men had ventured to go abroad, "out of books and out of themselves, to work among God's creatures . . . every age had abounded with excellent inventions, and every year might perhaps do so," if proper provision were made.

Influence of the Dreamers

Clearly from the time of Queen Elizabeth, Sir Humphrey Gilbert and Sir Francis Bacon down to the time of the first meetings of the Royal Society after the Restoration, when Cowley published his proposal, men were increasingly critical of the education of their day. Whether that education was of the young apprentices to trades, or of the sons of the gentry at Oxford or Cambridge, men claimed that time was being wasted, new ideas were being disregarded and opportunities for much greater and more rapid progress were being lost, as well as a possible gain in wealth and comfort that might be achieved from that knowledge. Emphasis on wit and memory might aid men to "steal from others' trunks" and borrow heavily from the books written by earlier generations; but it certainly did not lead to digging deep into the new mines for the gold of new learning.

Such digging could best be done not by one man or a few alone, but by a well-organized and well-equipped group with plenty of capital,—for equipment was costly. These men were not to limit themselves to the study of books, though that was essential as part of their work. They were to travel and to observe, to test the truth of matters for themselves, and to report their findings for the common good. The learned men of the schools had missed much that the workers in the trades and crafts already had found out. The new philosophers must also study the manual arts and consult with the artisans as well as with the scholars. Finally, facts alone were not enough; their significance in relation to other facts and hypotheses must be sought out. For that, men must work together to amass the evidence on which the geniuses among them could theorize.

Bacon's ultimate aim was the advancement of learning and only secondarily the greater usefulness of what might be discovered. In the England of expanding trade and wealth characterizing the early seventeenth century, Hartlib, Petty, Cowley and, to a less degree, Evelyn saw that practical values to be gained from experimental knowledge were fully as important as the theoretical. Cowley even wrote that the profits from the discoveries and inventions to be made at his proposed college would soon more than cover its costs.

The schemes of all these men were destined not to be carried out as they had devised them; but they served as ferments, stimulating men's thought and conversation and helping to make the intellectual atmosphere of the mid-seventeenth century favorable to the formation and development of some organization for the promotion of natural knowledge. As the early years of the Royal Society unfold, one finds a definite attempt on the part of the Society to carry out projects proposed in various of these schemes, as the writing of the histories of trades and the sending of questions, if not of philosophers themselves, to foreign countries for investigation and report. The Society used the direct study of nature with the reading of earlier records only as a check upon present work. It sought to provide and to improve equipment. It recognized the importance of cooperative effort in the study of a problem.

Dreams about these and similar activities are embedded in old books that nowadays are rarely opened, but they have done their work. They have helped to shape the thinking of the men who formed the Royal Society and who shared in its activities.

3

THE VIRTUOSI

SIR FRANCIS BACON'S books and the schemes proposed by various writers were ideas on paper. Other men, like Sir Thomas Gresham in Sir Humphrey Gilbert's time, were not content with the written word but put their ideas into action. Thus Gresham College and later "the invisible college"[1] came into being. Both of these very different "colleges" played an important part in the early history of the Royal Society. Accordingly, their origins and development need to be considered.

Another factor also needing consideration arose out of the great interest many of the wealthy in that age took in collecting objects of varied kinds. At first concerned mainly with things they considered of historical or artistic value, many soon became collectors of "rareties" as well,—strange or curious objects from foreign lands, and mathematical or mechanical novelties. Out of such collections as these were to arise eventually the great museums of today.

[1] See below, note p. 35.

In the seventeenth century they were the recreation of amateurs, science-lovers but not scientists. The virtuosi, as they and their friends were called in those days, for all their amateurishness and their naïveté, in their enthusiasm for the "new philosophy" of scientific study provided the rich soil out of which the Royal Society was to develop and true science to grow.

The founding of Gresham College takes us back again to the days of Queen Elizabeth, though its helpful influence upon the development of science was not of importance until later in the next century. Sir Thomas Gresham, a London merchant and Queen Elizabeth's financial agent, was seriously concerned about the poor educational opportunities for the Londoners of his day, just as Sir Humphrey Gilbert had been. Without waiting for government money and support, Sir Thomas provided in his will that after his death and that of his wife, his London mansion and all his estate should be turned over to the City of London and to the Mercers Guild, in trust for the citizens, to provide them with lecturers and a place of assembly. This was done and in 1598 Gresham College opened as Sir Thomas had planned it.

What we now know as adult education was unheard of in those days. There were no public museums and art galleries with people on their staffs to explain the exhibits and to give public lectures from their special knowledge. Nor were the grammar schools expected to train young people after they were thirteen or fourteen if they stayed that long. Those who could afford it and who were ambitious for their sons' advancement might employ tutors for them, and either send them on to one of the colleges in Oxford or Cambridge, or on a grand tour of Europe for a couple of years or so.

But most boys went to work as soon as they were in their teens. They would be apprenticed to some master craftsman for seven years in order to learn a trade while earning their board and lodging. Those who wanted to enter the professions and become teachers, clergymen, doctors or lawyers had of course somehow to get training in one or other of the two universities. There were scholarships even then to help the poor but brilliant boy along, or he might attract the favorable notice of a powerful man who would give him opportunity for advancement.

The medical student, for example, after getting his bachelor's degree in arts, then had to study six years more for his degree in medicine, attending two dissections in that time, and taking part in a public debate. Before becoming a doctor of medicine he had to study five more years, attend three dissections and take part in more public discussions of medical matters. This study was not like that of medical students today. It meant reading the ancient books on medicine, some of them written fifteen hundred years before, listening to lectures on these books and their writers and then passing examinations on them. Medical students then did not take care of patients under supervision nor work in a laboratory or hospital nor pay attention, if they were not interested, to any of the advances in medical knowledge of their day. The kind of topics they discussed in public debates were such, we are told, as: Is it possible for man to live without breath? Are all parts of the body nourished by the blood? (They argued "yes" for the first question and "no" for the second.) Really to learn about patients and their ailments, a young medical student would do as well if not better to get himself apprenticed to some experienced doctor and to assist him in his work. Such medical training was common well into the nineteenth century.

Gresham College

Sir Thomas Gresham knew that most of the citizens of London would never go abroad or even to Oxford or Cambridge to study. Instead, he brought the professors and the lectures to them. In his house, hereafter Gresham College, seven unmarried professors were to live in comfortable quarters and each was to be paid a salary of fifty pounds a year. There were to be professors of law, physic, rhetoric, divinity, music, geometry and astronomy as in the universities generally in the middle ages. Each was to give a stated series of lectures three times a year, the science lectures alternately in Latin and in English, the others in Latin, and the citizens of London were to be welcome to attend.

The Mercers Company and the mayor and aldermen of the City of London, having asked the two old universities for nominations for these professorships, appointed such able men that from the outset a high standard was set. The lectures attracted to the assembly place the leading men in London,—courtiers and nobles, business men and company members, as well as doctors, clergymen, mathematicians and other scholars. The mansion house, well located in the heart of the City, was solidly enough built so that it lasted for more than two centuries. It was easily accessible and very large, with beautiful grounds and gardens. Small wonder that after a professor's lecture, his friends and admirers would linger on in the gardens or in his rooms, discussing together.

Notable men accepted these professorships. When Oxford wanted its first appointee for the new Savilian professorship in 1619, it took the Gresham professor of geometry from London, Henry Briggs, one of the ablest mathematicians of his time. He was the Briggs who computed the Briggsian tables of logarithms and helped to popularize their use by scientists, teaching "the meaning and the use of this booke at Gresham house." Another noted mathematician at Gresham College was William Oughtred who invented two forms of slide rules, and who also had among his private pupils Seth Ward and John Wallis, later themselves to be leaders in the scientific world.

By virtue of their official position and their location in the City, these Gresham professors were in close association with the sea captains, the shipbuilders and the administrative officials of the English Navy. Their learning was not just for the lecture halls but had practical value as well. Already we see developing some of the major characteristics that differentiate modern scientific growth from the greatness of Greek scientific work. These Gresham professors did not scorn association with so-called practical men; they were willing to work on practical problems themselves. They not only cooperated with other men of like mind, but they sought their help and used their experience as a basis for their own theories which they again put to the test of practical use.

Regardless of the death of Queen Elizabeth in 1603 and the struggles and difficulties of the Stuart kings, James I and Charles I, her successors on the throne, Gresham College continued on its way. Later, as we shall see, its professors were to be among the group of science-lovers agreeing to organize formally, its apartments were to be the place where organization was agreed upon, and Gresham College was to house the young Royal Society and its collections for many years. In fact the two institutions were often confused even then; the Fellows of the Society were referred to as Greshamites, and Gresham College and the Royal Society were names used interchangeably although mistakenly.

England Under Charles I

While Gresham College was proceeding with its scheduled program in the heart of the City, the tension between the first Stuart kings and their subjects tightened almost to the breaking point of actual bloodshed. Charles I needed money. His parliaments would not grant him funds until he had first redressed their grievances. Therefore Charles ruled without parliament for a number of years, collecting revenue from whatever sources he could. He made the people of the inland cities pay the ancient ship-money tax, till then levied only on the sea-coast towns for their protection,—and then he spent the money for his court instead of for ships. He sold to companies of business men the privilege of holding a monopoly on the sale of products the people wanted. His favorite courtiers were unpopular with the people, and his queen was a French woman, a Roman Catholic in a country which a hundred years earlier had severed relations with the Roman Catholic Church and did not wish now to have them resumed. In foreign affairs also Charles was treating with the hated Spanish, instead of fighting against them as the English had done in the time of "good Queen Bess."

Affairs on the continent of Europe were in a turmoil. The terrible Thirty Years War was ravaging the Germanies as Bohemians and Swedes, Dutch and French fought the Holy Roman Emperor and his armies, Spanish as well as Austrian and German. Deeply involved in the struggle was the whole problem of the relation between the Pope as head of the Catholic Church and the Protestant leaders, supporters of separate or of state churches. Many men wanted to share in the great wealth and in the vast lands formerly owned by the Church and now seized from the Church in those countries that would no longer recognize the authority of the Pope. Small wonder was it that the Pilgrim Fathers, seeing the end of peace between tolerant Holland and Catholic Spain, left their refuge in Leyden and in 1620 founded Plymouth in the New World to establish homes where they could worship God in their own way, far from warring states.

Nor was it strange that men of various European countries, especially if they happened to have Protestant leanings, found England a pleasant place to come to even under the early Stuart rulers. While large sections of the continent were battle-grounds, England was at peace,—for the time being. Samuel Hartlib, as we have seen, came from Danzig in the 1620s and stayed in England until his death. Henry Oldenburg, of whom more later, came from Bremen several times on missions of one sort or another, until he too came to stay. Theodore Haak, a Calvinist from Worms, came in 1625 for a year at the universities. He returned three years later for the rest of his days, his mastery of languages making him useful as a translator. From France came the Calvinist physician, Pierre Moulin, on visits to the London of James I; his sons, Peter and Louis, came back to England to remain.

These men, and others like them, were helpful in the development of the new science for they brought with them word of what was being done on the continent by science-lovers there. They wrote letters back and forth conveying news of science as well as of politics, business and religion. They helped to translate English publications into French and Latin. They told what they had seen being done by European science-lovers and made helpful suggestions to their English friends. Haak, for example, was the one who suggested the formation of "the invisible college," the forerunner of the Royal Society.

Though there were no newspapers as yet, even then a net-work of communications linked England with the European countries. Men went abroad on government or on private business and brought back European books as well as news. Students wandered from university to university in Italy, France, Holland. Men, exiled to foreign cities, when restored to favor, brought back with them new tastes, new ideas, new interests learned abroad. Thus many a Royalist supporter, in exile with the Stuart prince, entertained himself as Sir Kenelm Digby did, with trying out some of the new chemical experiments, studying the stars with the new spy-glass, and learning more about the herbs or simples and the drugs of the day. Even Charles II during his years of exile had a work-shop or laboratory of his own, and upon his restoration to the English throne, set up a laboratory in his palace. Like Samuel Hartlib's "chemical son," king and commoner alike were intensely interested in the scientific wonders being discovered in their time.

Collectors of Curiosities

Some of this enthusiasm expressed itself in collections of curiosities like the collections of a small boy. Travelers had seen and admired the great Renaissance collections of Italy and France, the remains of the ancient Greek and Roman civilizations, their coins, their statues, their books, now so carefully preserved. England too had curious old Roman relics. In the early Stuart days the nobles and men of wealth became ardent collectors not only of the objects of antiquity—marbles, coins, medals—but also of "rareties," some of them curiosities that we might call just trash. When the Royal Society had been under way only a few years, it named one of the Fellows a benefactor because from his own collections he had presented to the "repository" of the Society among other things, "a wind-gun, a burning-glass in a brass frame," and one in a wooden frame, "a piece of petrified wood, a cocoa-nut, an ostrich's egg-shell," "a strange bone with a rib in the middle," "a geometrical arch composed of many small pieces of wood without nails or pins", a loadstone (magnet), "a scales for weighing gold without any counterpoise" and "two papers of petrified grass" (Nov. 4, 1663). From such beginnings did the great museums of natural history develop.

One significance that the collections had for these amateurs, the virtuosi, was the value of the specimens in revealing to the beholder the wonders of the world created by Divine Providence. They were a revelation of God's power and His glory expressed in the natural world as His power and His glory were revealed in the books of the Bible. The "admirable contrivance of natural things" made a great impression on the virtuosi who first examined through the early compound microscope the eye of a small fly, "the inimitable gildings and embroideries" in the smallest plant seeds, and "the accurate order and symmetry in the frame of the most minute creatures." Dr.

John Wilkins was a bishop in the Church of England when he wrote those words in a book on theology. His first work with the microscope had been done at least ten years earlier, but he had not forgotten his first impressions.

For men for whom in those times religious beliefs and church doctrines might at any moment become matters of life and death, observation and study of such natural objects, they claimed, had a definite religious value. They earnestly rejected any suggestion that such scientific study was harmful to religious beliefs, no matter what their critics might say about its possible destructiveness to accepted religious doctrines. The deeper the knowledge they had of the creature, the deeper the reverence and respect they felt for its Creator. Why should not God's power be learned from the natural world as well as from the Bible?

It seemed well worth while for sober respectable churchmen to give much time to such a profitable as well as fascinating study as that of the natural world in which they lived. Not only would it profit their souls but also it might profit their purses because of the everyday uses to which such increased knowledge could be put. Especially to the practical minded, moderate Puritan in the troubled times of Cromwell and in the laxity and dissoluteness of court life under the Stuarts, this new philosophy, this natural science, was a profitable, leisure-time activity. It appealed to the intellect; it strengthened religious beliefs; it contributed to the common welfare through its practical usefulness; and besides, it was a subject of great delight.

Small wonder, then, that among the amateurs were to be found many Puritans and that some of them, like Dr. Wilkins, became leaders in organizing the Royal Society for promoting Natural Knowledge. The challenge to the authority of the Pope in the Catholic Church and of the bishops in the Anglican Church and the appeal to the sources, to the Bible rather than to the Church Fathers—these were now being carried over from the ecclesiastical and political realms into the intellectual and scientific ones. Aristotle and Galen were no longer to be the final authority, if observation and experiment proved them to be mistaken. No longer should questions be settled by authority if the facts proved otherwise. These active-minded, independent Puritans were willing to take risks if the stakes were high enough. They had done so in government and church, why not in laboratories and lecture-halls? So they tested and experimented for themselves, already carrying out the spirit of the future Royal Society's motto, "Nullius in verba." [2]

Virtuosi

These collectors of rarities in the earlier part of the century, whether Puritan or Anglican, nobles or professional men, were satisfying their curiosity rather than attempting to pursue scientific learning. It was a recreation in which they delighted, not an activity to which they devoted their whole time and thought. At first they were antiquarians in their concern with the relics of the past, glad to possess "the great silver box that Nero kept his beard in" or "the urn that did contain the ashes of the emperors." Gradually some of these gentlemen became more and more interested in mechanical and mathematical notions. Some, to be sure, were problems the Greeks and the Romans had worked on and that men had puzzled over ever since, like the problem of perpetual motion. Other problems stemmed from the genius of Galileo in Italy and Descartes in France.

Mathematical Magick was more than the title of a book written in the sixteen-forties by one of the virtuosi. It expressed the feeling of many about the "marvels" of those days. According to its author, Dr. Wilkins, even one man by the aid of a series of wheels, ropes, and pulleys properly arranged with his breath alone could uproot the

2 "Not under bond to abide by any master's authority"; translated from Horace's *Epistles* I, 1, line 14, in I. Masson; *Three Centuries of Chemistry.* (New York, [1925]) p. 44, note.

largest tree. (See Plate 5.) The ancients had known the principle of the lever; he and men of similar ingenuity could find many practical uses for it, for the wheel, the wedge, the screw. "A chariot with sails to catch the wind," an "ark for submarine navigation," a "talking image" were some of his suggested "automata." There is no record that Dr. Wilkins attempted to make them himself, though his father, a goldsmith, had a "very mechanical head" and "was much for trying experiments," according to one of Wilkins' friends.

Gradually these scientific notions became more engrossing, displacing earlier interest in antiquities. The word "virtuosi," earlier applied to these gentlemen collectors, after 1640 began rather to mean a man who observed facts and collected specimens as a basis for the study of the mathematical and mechanical arts and of natural history. Such study, as Sprat pointed out in his *History* some years later, was a proper one for gentlemen of leisure, well within their capacities and sweeter than academic learning because it had objects they could see and feel, and a method they could understand. Thus art was giving way to science, under the pressure of Bacon's influence and the example of some of the leading men, patrons of the virtuosi as well as virtuosi themselves. Not least among them all was Charles II himself.

These enthusiasts, however, were not scientists yet but amateurs or lovers of science. Their object, according to Sprat, was rather to make collections of "curiosities to adorn cabinets and gardens than for the solidity of philosophical discoveries." But the help they gave to the true scientists lay in their eager cooperation, expressed in financial form as well as in friendship and patronage. They provided a welcoming audience for the new discoveries and they formed a group where ideas could be exchanged, experiments tried out, and scientific news from abroad and at home disseminated. These amateurs were of major importance in the early development of modern science.

"The Invisible College" [3]

By 1645 some of the younger men among these newer virtuosi, science-lovers that they were, had come together in a kind of luncheon club in London at one of the taverns, where they met weekly to discuss scientific news. One of its members, Robert Boyle, referred to it in his letters as "the invisible college,"—a meeting place for serious study without buildings or professors,—and as "the invisible college" it has been known to this day. Years after the group had broken up, almost all of its members having become Fellows of the Royal Society that ultimately succeeded it, Dr. John Wallis wrote down in 1678 his recollections of those early days in a passage that has often been quoted and is well worth quoting again:

I take its [the Royal Society's] first Ground and Foundation to have been in London about the year 1645 (if not sooner) when the same Dr. Wilkins (then Chaplain to the Prince Elector Palatine, in London), Dr. Jonathan Goddard, Dr. Ent (now Sir George Ent), Dr. Glisson, Dr. Scarbrough (now Sir Charles Scarbrough), Dr. Merrit, with myself and some others, met weekly (sometimes at Dr. Goddard's Lodgings, sometimes at the Mitre in Wood-street hard by) at a certain day and hour, under a certain Penalty, and a weekly Contribution for the Charge of Experiments, with certain Rules agreed upon amongst us. Where (to avoid diversion to other discourses, and for some other reasons) we barred all Discourses of Divinity, of State-Affairs, and of News (other than what concern'd our business of Philosophy) confining our selves to Philosophical Inquiries, and such as related thereunto; as Physick, Anatomy, Geometry, Astronomy, Navigation, Staticks, Mechanicks, and Natural Experiments. We there discoursed the Circulation of the

[3] Attention should be called to Miss R. H. Syfret's important article on "The Origins of the Royal Society," *Notes and Records of the Royal Society*, V, no. 2 (April, 1948), 75-137. Miss Syfret raises the question whether Boyle's term, "the invisible college," refers to the scientific club or rather to Hartlib's Comenian schemes. Haak would then be the major link between pansophism and the club of which he was admittedly the instigator. Unfortunately Miss Syfret's article was received too late to be considered in this book.

Blood, the Valves in the Veins, the Copernican Hypothesis, the Nature of Comets and new Stars, the Attendants on Jupiter, the Oval shape of Saturn, the Inequalities and Selenography of the Moon, the several Phases of Venus and Mercury, the Improvement of Telescopes, and Grinding of Glasses for that purpose (wherein Dr. Goddard was particularly ingaged, and did maintain an Operator in his house for that purpose), the weight of the Air, the Possibility or Impossibility of Vacuities, and Nature's abhorrence thereof, the Torricellian Experiment in Quicksilver, the Descent of Heavy Bodies, and the Degrees of Acceleration therein, with others of like nature. Some of which were but new discoveries, and others not so generally known and embraced as now they are.

These meetings we removed, soon after, to the Bull-head in Cheapside and (in Term-time) to Gresham Colledge, where we met weekly at Mr. Foster's Lecture (the Astronomy-Professor there) and after the Lecture ended, repaired sometimes to Mr. Foster's Lodgings, sometimes to some other place not far distant, where we continued such Inquiries; and our Numbers encreased.

This passage tells us a number of interesting things, when we translate its terms into modern phraseology and relate its information to the history of the period,—about the members of "the invisible college," their meeting-places, and their subjects for discussion.

Dr. Wallis here names eight members of the group including himself and Mr. Samuel Foster, the Gresham professor of astronomy. In a much later "Account of some Passages in his own Life" written in 1697, Dr. Wallis in repeating much of this story adds to it the name of Theodore Haak, "a German of the Palatinate, and then resident in London, who, I think, gave the first occasion, and first suggested those meetings." A tenth member, as we know from his letters regretting his missing certain of the meetings of "the invisible college," was the Honorable Robert Boyle.

Except for Boyle, these men were all university trained, professional men,—doctors, clergymen, linguists. Only Boyle was the son of a nobleman and he alone had first studied at Eton and then abroad for some years with a tutor. Nine of these men were therefore in all probability already friends from their college days together or from having had a common college and theological background. Wilkins and Goddard had been at Magdalen Hall in Oxford at the same time, and Merrit and Haak had attended Gloucester Hall there, both notable Puritan centers. The five others were Cambridge men, two from Caius, Harvey's college where the medical tradition was very strong, two from Emanuel, the Puritan stronghold in Cambridge, and Ent from Sidney Sussex where Cromwell had gone. They were relatively young men also, ranging in age in 1645 from Boyle, the youngest at eighteen, to Dr. Glisson, the oldest at forty-eight. Three were in their late twenties, two more in their early thirties.

Drawn to London by their various professions and activities, seven of them at least were supporters of the parliamentary party in the struggle with the king, and only one, Dr. Scarbrough, was a pronounced Royalist. Strongly Puritan in education and interests, Haak was employed by the Westminster Assembly to translate for them the Dutch annotations to the Bible, and Dr. John Wilkins was the chaplain in England for the Prince Elector Palatine who was next heir to the English throne if the Stuart line failed to win the battle with the parliamentary party over the divine right of kings.

Good reason was it, therefore, in those uncertain times that these congenial spirits should debar from their friendly gatherings any discussion of politics, religion or the news of the day. Such subjects were too hotly controversial and too general elsewhere. Far better that they should stick to their common interest, natural philosophy. Discussions about the map of the moon or the possibility of creating a vacuum and similar objective matters were far safer and certainly more fruitful topics for consideration than Cromwell's activities, for instance, and equally as precedent-breaking. Church and state could well be disregarded for one day a week.

After this luncheon club began meeting regularly, Dr. Wallis reported that they came together either at a tavern or at Dr. Goddard's house, and shortly thereafter during term-time at Gresham College after Mr. Foster's astronomy lecture. One advantage of Dr. Goddard's house lay in the fact that he employed a technician, as we would say today, an assistant who could grind glass into lenses. Also, Dr. Goddard as a physician would have a store of various herbs and drugs with which they could experiment in his own private workshop. Taverns did not have such conveniences. On the other hand, Gresham College had not only its lecture halls for their use but its gardens, its astronomical equipment, its books and above all its seven professors at least five of whom a few years later were to become charter members of the new Royal Society. The older College was a hospitable host and friend to these amateurs of "the invisible college."

The Century of Scientific Genius

The friends had much to discuss, as Dr. Wallis enumerated, ranging from Galileo's discoveries in 1609-1611 with his newly devised telescope to his studies of matter in motion and the laws concerning it. Old Aristotelian and Ptolemaic conceptions of the perfection of the heavens and of the position of the universe had been dramatically proved false by Galileo's discovery that the planet Jupiter, like the earth with its moon, had satellites swinging around it, and that the planets Mercury and Venus, far from resembling billiard balls, and ever the same, went through phases as the moon did, by virtue of their paths or orbits lying within that of the earth's around the sun. Even that most perfect celestial body, the sun, had spots on it, and the moon as seen through a telescope had all sorts of irregularities and roughnesses apparent on its surface. Most startling of all was the proof by analogy these discoveries added to the Copernican theory that the earth was merely one of the planets and that the sun, not the earth, was the center of the universe. If man's home, the earth, was whirling through space, how did man stick on it? And how much less important the earth and its inhabitants were than all the learned men had claimed through ages past! Might there not be men on other planets? And were they Jews and Christians too? These new astronomical theories involved much more than physics, mathematics and astronomy. Grave questions of religion and philosophy were opened up also.

Then there were the new discoveries in the anatomical and physiological fields, greatly stimulated by Vesalius' studies of the human frame (*De Fabrica Humani Corporis*) published in 1543, the same year in which Copernicus had published his masterly *De Revolutionibus*. These two great books, each revolutionary in its field, have made 1543 generally recognized as the birth-year of modern science.

Doctors in Italy carrying on Vesalius' work had found the valves in the veins. William Harvey, after studying with these Italians, had returned to England to prove to his own satisfaction that the blood circulated through the arteries and back through the veins to the heart again. Instead of being a kind of hearth-fire to warm the blood, the heart in reality was a pump. Harvey did not have the microscope with which to observe the tiny capillaries connecting the arteries and the veins, but he argued from his evidence that some such connection must exist. Fifty years later Malpighi was to observe them for the first time. After Harvey had published his work in 1628, his practice as a doctor fell off seriously because people could not believe that any doctor holding notions so contrary to the age-old teachings could be a reliable physician. So Harvey told Aubrey who wrote it down. Fortunately the doctor lived long enough (till 1657) to see his theory of the circulation of the blood generally accepted. The young virtuosi, several of them doctors themselves, would surely find much to discuss.

Then too there was the singular behavior of quick-silver,

as they called mercury, in experiments Torricelli in Italy and Pascal in France were making with a new device, a barometer, to show differences in the weight of air, or atmospheric pressure. What an astounding idea that air had weight which could be measured and that its weight on mountain-tops varied from that in mines and caves. Could a pump really remove air, if it had weight and substance, from an enclosed vessel and thus create that vacuum which Nature abhorred, according to all previous knowledge?

Also Galileo's book on mechanics and the laws of motion (*Dialoghi Delle Nuove Scienze*) had only recently been published (1636). That made the subject of matter in motion a lively topic for discussion in more ways than one. Galileo had put to the test of experiment the statements of the ancient authorities and had found them incorrect, like that one about a heavy weight falling faster than a light one. What about the speed and the path of objects such as cannon-balls shot out of catapults in the old days and out of guns nowadays?

Harvey and Galileo are only two of the six or seven geniuses of the greatest importance that this seventeenth century was to produce, not to mention a number of other scientists of hardly less importance. This "century of genius" [4] with its Newton and Boyle, its Kepler and its Gilbert, its Harvey and Galileo, had Descartes and Pascal, Torricelli, Wren, Hooke and Halley as well, and many more besides. They and their fellow-workers were rapidly devising the instruments of precision they needed and were developing the scientific methods that Bacon had proclaimed. Galileo had constructed his telescope according to the laws of perspective as he knew them, after he had heard of such an invention by a Dutch lens-maker, and with his mathematical and mechanical genius made better and more powerful ones. Then he had systematically used this new tool. Harvey had demonstrated the circulation of

[4] So named by Professor A. N. Whitehead, *Science and the Modern World* (New York, 1926) Chap. III.

42

the blood by a series of experiments planned precisely to prove quantitatively that the body contained just so much blood and that it must be pumped by the heart through the body in a continuous circuit, for the heart muscle contracted and expanded every second as long as life was in it. No guess work this, but the first carefully planned experiment to prove a physiological fact mathematically and quantitatively.

William Gilbert, Queen Elizabeth's physician, had published his epochal study of terrestrial magnetism (*De Magnete*) in 1600, a fact that helps to explain the virtuosi's great interest in loadstones or magnets in the middle decades of that century. Kepler's formulation of the laws of planetary motion, together with Galileo's brilliant work in astronomy and mechanics, was combined by Newton with the Copernican hypothesis in his fundamental theory of the universe. The laws of attraction and of motion, mathematically demonstrated, governed earth, planets and stars alike in one magnificently ordered system.

Other astronomers like Edmond Halley and Flamsteed in England by their studies supplied supporting evidence. Halley in particular gave the death-blow to one popular superstition about comets heralding disaster when he predicted that the comet of 1682 would return in 1759. It came when he predicted it would. Men now recognize "Halley's comet" as having shone in 1066 when the Normans invaded England. We have seen it in 1910 and others will see it in 1985.

Robert Boyle, the finest virtuoso of them all, for the first time distinguished between element, compound and mixture and used his improved air-pump to work out the law of gases that students know today as Boyle's Law. Robert Hooke was his right-hand man in this work, and then as curator for the Royal Society moved on into a bewildering variety of activities as he helped the eager members carry out their experiments and at the same time worked out his own. His inventions were many, from the universal joint to the main-spring for watches, and his

published observations with the early compound microscope are the classic in that field.

Great as was the work of Hooke, Halley, Torricelli and
many another scientist in Europe during the seventeenth
century, all are overshadowed by the towering achievements of Kepler and Galileo, Gilbert, Harvey and Boyle,
and most of all, of Newton.

Inventions

The seventeenth century was not yet half over, however, and much of this work was still to come, when the
virtuosi of "the invisible college" held their discussions.
Still, they had plenty of important ideas to discuss and
instruments to improve if they could. The first compound
microscopes, the barometer, the air-pump, the pendulum-
clock for the accurate measure of time, a machine for
grinding lenses, crude thermometers,—these were only
some of the instruments of precision these amateurs were
seeing developed, in some cases helping in their development. Mathematicians and astronomers rejoiced in the
new-made tables of logarithms which saved them endless
hours of calculation. They began to use Descartes' proposals for a more systematic expression of mathematical
ideas, as for example, that the first letters of the alphabet
could be used to express known quantities and the last
letters to express the unknown. Even calculating machines
seemed a possibility to these mechanical geniuses later on
in this century; both Pascal and Leibnitz actually made
them. The seventeenth century, as well as the twentieth,
had its mechanical and technological triumphs that greatly
aided the advance of science.

But while these science-lovers shut themselves off from
debate about contemporary politics for at least one day a
week, events caught up with them. Civil war had broken
out between king and parliament. The Royalists had been
defeated and the King had fled, later to be captured and

turned over for trial and execution. Meanwhile the parliamentary commissioners were ruling the country and the King's supporters had to leave their government positions, if they did not actually have to flee from the country. Oxford had been loyal to him; the heads of its various colleges either had to make their peace with parliament or leave. Some left and the commissioners replaced them with their own adherents. Consequently several members of "the invisible college" in 1648 and 1649 were chosen to succeed these Royalists and left London for Oxford. Dr. John Wilkins went to Wadham College to be its head or warden, Dr. Jonathan Goddard and Dr. John Wallis went to other colleges to be followed shortly by several of their friends.

Those left in London continued with their meetings while the Oxford members joined with them from time to time when they were in the City, but "the invisible college" did not thrive. Too many important members were in other parts of the realm and Cromwell's soldiers were too conspicuous in London. It was mainly at Oxford during these Cromwellian years that the amateurs—the virtuosi—with their friends kept alive their scientific pursuits.

4

THE FOUNDING OF THE ROYAL SOCIETY

D R. JOHN WALLIS after describing the meetings of "the invisible college" in the passage already quoted in the last chapter, continued his account as follows:

About the years 1648, 1649, some of our Company were removed to Oxford; (first, Dr. Wilkins, then I, soon after Dr. Goddard); whereupon our Company divided. Those at London (and we, when we had occasion to be there) met as before. Those of us at Oxford with Dr. Ward (now Bishop of Salisbury), Dr. Petty (now Sir William Petty), Dr. Bathurst, Dr. Willis and many others of the most inquisitive Persons in Oxford, met weekly (for some years) at Dr. Petty's Lodgings on the like account; (to wit, so long as Dr. Petty continued in Oxford, and for some while after) because of the conveniences we had there, (being the House of an Apothecary) to view and make use, of Drugs, and other like matters, as there was occasion.

Our Meetings there were very numerous, and very considerable. For, beside the diligence of Persons, studiously Inquisitive, the Novelty of the Design made many to resort thither; who when it ceased to be new, began to grow more remiss, or did pursue such Inquiries at Home.

We did afterwards (Dr. Petty being gone for Ireland, and our numbers growing less) remove thence. And (some years before His Majesty's Return) did meet (as Dr. Holder observes), at Dr. Wilkins' Lodgings in Wadham-Colledge.

But before the time he mentions [1659] those set Meetings ceased in Oxford, and were held in London. Where (after the death of Mr. Foster) we continued to meet at Gresham-Colledge (as before), at Mr. Rooke's Lecture, (who succeeded Mr. Foster) and from thence repaired to some convenient place in or near that Colledge: And so onward; till the Fire of London, caused our removal to Arundel-house; from thence we are since returned to Gresham-Colledge again.

In the meanwhile; our Company at Gresham-Colledge, being much again increased, by the accession of divers Eminent and Noble Persons upon His Majesties Return; we were (about the beginning of the Year 1662) by His Majesties Grace and Favour, Incorporated by the name of the Royal Society, etc.

Many years later Dr. Wallis enlarged this account with the statement that after Dr. Wilkins was transferred to Trinity College, Cambridge, and before they returned to London, the Oxford Society met at the lodgings of the Honorable Mr. Robert Boyle "then resident for divers years in Oxford."

The Oxford Philosophical Society

Unlike the informality of "the invisible college" of 1645, the Oxford amateurs formally organized themselves in 1651 into the Philosophical Society of Oxford and kept regular minutes of their meetings. Despite the return of some of its leaders to London, the Oxford Society continued to hold meetings, with no great regularity, however, until 1690 when they ceased altogether. Oxford still treasures that minute book. Probably the formal organization and record-keeping of the Philosophical Society set the precedent later for the organization of the Royal Society, just as "the invisible college" had first set the pattern for regular meetings for scientific discussion and experiment. The virtuosi were becoming better trained in organized activity as they moved from "the invisible college" in London in the sixteen-forties to the Philosophical Society in Oxford of the sixteen-fifties and on to the Royal Society in London of the sixteen-sixties.

The first years of the Oxford Philosophical Society were its most notable. Oxford in that decade was a little outside of the turmoil in London where Oliver Cromwell was ruling first with and then without the help of even a rump parliament. By 1658, the science-lovers remaining in London had to cease from meeting, for Gresham College had been made a temporary barracks for soldiers and they did not wish, Sprat wrote to his friend, Kit Wren, to run the risk of suffering the fate of Archimedes. The virtuosi were too well trained in the classics not to remember that story of how the greatest mathematical and mechanical genius of the Greeks and the Romans, Archimedes, came to his death at the hands of Roman soldiers during the siege of the city of Syracuse. He was so absorbed in his mathematical problems, so one story ran, that he did not know when the city fell nor notice the soldiers when they invaded his room. So they struck him down. Naturally the virtuosi had no desire to have their scientific interests betray them to Cromwell's men in the same way!

Thus Oxford and especially Wadham College under the tolerant wardenship of the genial and greatly loved Dr. John Wilkins was a haven for the sons of Cavalier and Roundhead alike, and for the older men too, who wanted to pursue their philosophical interests in congenial company. Urged on by Warden Wilkins, Robert Boyle moved to Oxford to live there a number of years till he finally settled down with his sister in London. Dr. William Petty had a house there. Seth Ward came in 1649 as the newly appointed Savilian professor of astronomy. Laurence Rooke was there before going to London to be astronomy professor at Gresham College. They all either lived at the

PLATE 5. "How any man may blow up the greatest oak with his breath"

(From Dr. John Wilkins' *Mathematical Magick*,
1680)

PLATE 6. Doctor John Wilkins as Bishop of Chester

(From *The Record of the Royal Society*, London, 1940, by
courtesy of the Royal Society)

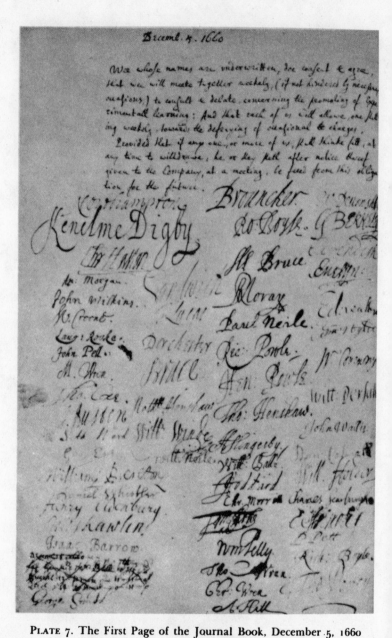

PLATE 7. The First Page of the Journal Book, December 5, 1660

(From *The Signatures of the First Journal Book and the Charter Book of the Royal Society*, London, 1912, by courtesy of the Royal Society)

College or came there often to be with its Warden, to see his curiosities and to talk with the brilliant lads then in the College.

The historian of Wadham College calls this "its most glorious period." Here were to be found among others "that miracle of a youth," Christopher Wren, his good friend Thomas Sprat, Walter Pope, the much younger half-brother of the Warden, later Gresham professor of astronomy, and the mathematician William Neile. Some of them later were bishops appointed by Charles II as well as Fellows of the Royal Society. There John Evelyn visited, recording in his diary his delight over Wren's precocious achievements as well as in Wilkins' entertainment and his notable collection of curiosities.

"We all dined," Evelyn wrote on July 13, 1654, "at the most obliging and universally-curious Dr. Wilkins's, at Wadham College. He was the first who showed me the transparent apiaries, which he had built like castles and palaces, and so ordered them one upon the other, as to take the honey without destroying the bees. These were adorned with a variety of dials, little statues, vanes, etc.; and, he was so abundantly civil, finding me pleased with them, to present me with one of the hives which he had empty, and which I afterwards had in my garden at Sayes Court, where it continued many years, and which his Majesty came on purpose to see and contemplate with much satisfaction. He had also contrived a hollow statue, which gave a voice and uttered words by a long concealed pipe that went into its mouth, whilst one speaks through it at a good distance. He had, above in his lodgings and gallery, variety of shadows, dials, perspectives, and many other artificial, mathematical, and magical curiosities, a way-wiser, a thermometer, a monstrous magnet, conic, and other sections, a balance on a demi-circle; most of them of his own, and that prodigious young scholar, Mr. Christopher Wren; who presented me with a piece of white marble which he had stained with a lively red, very deep, as beautiful as if it had been natural."

Warden Wilkins' marriage in 1653 to Robina Cromwell, youngest sister of Oliver Cromwell and widow of Dr. Peter French, soon brought the Warden into even greater social prominence, making him more influential than he was already by reason of his several books on scientific subjects and on theology, and by his official position in Oxford. When Richard Cromwell succeeded his father Oliver as ruler of England, Dr. Wilkins was much in London as one of his close advisers during his brief rule. Then came Wilkins' appointment to the mastership of Trinity College, Cambridge, the most important university position in those days. But after a short eleven months there he was ejected in his turn to make way for a Royalist to be reinstated upon the Restoration of Charles II in 1660. Wilkins' interests and his positions combined with his "gentlemanlike behaviour" and his helpfulness to the younger virtuosi made him easily chief among them as well as an acknowledged leader in their societies, and he had powerful friends at court. When he returned to London that summer of 1660 naturally he rejoined the virtuosi there. In fact he presided at the November meeting when they decided to organize formally under the King's patronage, if that were possible.

The Formation of the Royal Society

Young Christopher Wren had been appointed Gresham professor of astronomy in 1657. After hearing him lecture on November 28, 1660, the virtuosi "did according to the usuall manner, withdraw for mutual converse where among other matters that were discoursed of, something was offered about a designe of Founding a College for the Promoting of Physico-Mathematicall Learning." After agreeing on an admission fee of ten shillings to defray occasional expenses, they drew up a list of forty names of "such persons as were known to those present, whom they judged willing and fit to joyne with them in their designe, who, if they should desire it, might be admitted before any other." So the old Journal-book read.

At the next week's meeting on December 5th, after hearing of the King's approval of their design, they signed the following statement:

Wee whose names are underwritten, doe consent to agree that wee will meete together Weekly (if not hindered by necessary Occasions) to consult and debate concerning the promoting of Experimentall learning; And that each of us will allowe, one shilling weekly, towards the defraying of occasional charges. Provided that if any one, or more of us, shall thinke fitt, at any time to withdrawe, he or they shall, after notice thereof given to the Company, at a meeting, be freed from this obligation for the future. (See Plate 7.)

The signatures of nearly all those listed at the previous meeting then follow (Wilkins fifth among them) together with seventy-three others, 115 in all. But at the next meeting they agreed to limit the number of members to fifty-five (a restriction soon disregarded) and to hold elections to memberships thereafter, with a quorum of twenty-one for that purpose. However, those of the nobility from barons up might be admitted as honorary members, if they so desired, as also were to be the professors of mathematics, physick and natural philosophy at the two universities. Upon the payment of the admission fee and the weekly charge for those meetings the professors could attend when they were in London. A suggestion was made that the new Society meet at the College of Physicians, but later that was dropped and the meetings were held at Gresham College.

The officers agreed upon at this meeting on December 12th were a president, to be chosen monthly, a treasurer and a register, both to serve for a year. In addition two servants were to be employed, an amanuensis or secretary, and an operator or technician. The register was to provide three books, one for the statutes and names of the Society, one for experiments and the results of debates, the third for occasional orders. Three members were to sit with the register at each meeting, take notes of important matters and together make up a report for filing. Thus were set up the charter-book and the journal-book of minutes, two of the most prized possessions of the Royal Society today.

The charter-book is particularly interesting, for from that day to this, no one has been deemed a Fellow of the Society until he has signed his name in that book, no matter when he was elected. On special pages are the names of the kings and queens who from Charles II (except for William and Mary and Anne) to George VI have been its patrons, and the names of the nobility who joined as honorary members. The long roll of the members or Fellows from the seventeenth century on down to the present has become a remarkable record of the greatest scientists in all fields, not alone from Britain but also from Europe and America.

But to return to the early days. A name for the new society still had not been chosen. Just as Boyle in his letters had given to the 1645 group the name "the invisible college" by which they have been known ever since, so now John Evelyn gave the new assembly its name. On December 3, 1661, he wrote in his diary: "By universal suffrage of our philosophic assembly, an order was made and register'd, that I should receive their public thanks for the honourable mention I made of them by the name of the Royal Society in my Epistle Dedicatory to the Lord Chancellor before my traduction of Naudeus.[1] Too great an honour for a trifle."

Charles II, Founder and Patron

King Charles had been taking considerable interest in the new organization. He had talked it over with two of its strongest supporters, Evelyn and Sir Robert Moray, who was both mathematician and courtier, as well as the

[1] *Instructions concerning Erecting of a Library by Gabriel Naudeus (Naudé)* translated by John Evelyn, 1661.

most frequently elected monthly president. When the Society petitioned in September 1661, for royal approval of incorporation, Charles quickly granted it. The charter finally passed the Great Seal on July 15, 1662, making that the official date for the founding of the Royal Society.

There is a story told early in the nineteenth century about the King having dined with the members of the Society on the night of its creation and having expressed his pleasure in being the first English monarch who had laid the foundation of such a society for an investigation into the secrets of nature. But Charles, however much a philosopher, was still more a wit, and with suitable gravity went on to say that among such learned men he now hoped for a solution to a question which had long puzzled him. "Suppose two pails of water were fixed in two different scales that were equally poised, and which weighed equally alike, and two small live fish were put into either of these pails, why should not that pail with such addition, weigh more than the other pail which stood against it?" Everyone sought to answer, but each gave a different opinion. One was so fantastic that another of the members burst into a loud laugh. The King insisted that he too give his opinion whereupon in plain terms he denied the fact. On which the King, "in high mirth" as the old author [2] expressed it, exclaimed, "Odds fish, brother, you are in the right!"

Whether true or not, the story is in keeping with Charles' attitude; for however much he enjoyed the company of these natural philosophers in the early years of his reign, he poked plenty of fun at their activities. He enjoyed a good laugh; but he was also generously disposed toward these over-serious enthusiasts.

The King in 1663 presented a mace to be carried before the president at meetings. (An old story, long since disproved, as Weld reported, by the finding of the royal warrant ordering it made, was that this was the mace of the House of Commons which Oliver Cromwell had had

2 I. D'Israeli.

thrown out as a "bauble.") Large and heavy, of silver gilt, beautifully wrought with roses and thistles, the harp and the fleur-de-lys, the royal monogram and the royal coat of arms, it bears also the coat of arms of the Society and a Latin inscription that it is the gift of Charles II, Founder and Patron. From that day to this, the mace is placed on the table in front of the president before the meeting begins.

Royal favor still was needed. The charter of 1662 proved within a short while not to be sufficient. Another was drawn up including the old one with additional privileges and that in turn passed the Great Seal on April 22, 1663. This second Charter is the one in which Charles II declared himself Founder and Patron of the Society. It has formed the basis of the organization ever since. Hereafter the Society was to be governed by a council of twenty-one members which included the president, a treasurer and two secretaries. All persons received into the Society within two months of the signing of this second charter were to be named Fellows of the Royal Society. Thus 119 men became the Original or Charter Fellows.

The Original Fellows

Their names make an interesting list. Among them are several members of the old "invisible college"—Boyle, Goddard, Seth Ward who by then was Bishop of Exeter, Ent, Theodore Haak, Sir William Petty, Wilkins and Wallis. The Oxford people are there, especially the Wadham College group—Christopher Wren and his cousin Matthew, Thomas Sprat, Walter Pope, William Neile, along with Robert Hooke, Boyle's skilled assistant in the Oxford days, and Henry Oldenburg, recently returned from years abroad as a tutor to Boyle's nephew. Five of the Gresham College professors are on the list, and Isaac Barrow from Cambridge. Among the eight or ten noblemen are George, Duke of Buckingham with chemical as well as court interests, and Lord Brouncker, first president of the Society and leading mathematician. Seth Ward was the only bishop then a Fellow, but a number of others, including Wilkins himself, were soon to be created bishops also. Doctors of medicine and doctors of divinity, lawyers, civil servants, literary men, are all there, also the shopkeeper, John Graunt, who was the first Englishman to publish a study of vital statistics based on the bills of mortality. Many like Evelyn, were true virtuosi, science-lovers. Yet hardly a third of the number could be called men of science, even if men like Wilkins, Evelyn and Petty are included; but among these men of science are some of the great names of that or of any era: Boyle, Wren, Hooke, Glisson, Wallis, Willughby.

An American eye reading the list catches the name of John Winthrop, governor of Connecticut and son of the first governor of Massachusetts. In London in the early sixties on his third visit there for business concerning the colonies, he had renewed his earlier associations with the virtuosi and thus became the first American Fellow of the Society as well as one of the Original Fellows. In spite of his heavy burden of business and state affairs, Winthrop was a remarkable man of science, credited with being the first chemist and metallurgist in the American colonies and one of the first physicians.

Long a correspondent of many of these men, upon his return to Connecticut after this visit, Winthrop became the western correspondent for the Society, writing many letters and sending back to the Society's "repository" or museum minerals, plants and various specimens of colonial curiosities. He was especially noted for having observed "a fifth satellite of Jupiter," and, uncertain whether it was a true satellite or a faint star close by, asked the astronomers among the Fellows in England for corroboration or correction. Not till the early twentieth century with its powerful telescopes was the faint fifth satellite officially identified. But in reporting his observation and requesting confirmation, Winthrop was proving himself a cautious and keen observer who systematically studied the stars even with the imperfect telescopes of 1664. He was a true science-lover and a valuable link between English and American scientists.

About a good many of these original Fellows little if anything is known today. Sprat described them as "gentlemen, free and unconfin'd" "who by the freedom of their education, the plenty of their estates and the usual generosity of noble bloud, may be well suppos'd to be most averse from sordid considerations." In modern English that might run, they were men of rank and title, not in any of the professions but well educated and with plenty of money, who had joined the Society not for the sake of making money out of the experiments nor of gaining special favors, but solely because they were interested in the advancement of learning for its own sake. These amateurs of science, together with the true scientists, were indeed a representative and notable group from the London society of the day. Within two or three years, after Charles II had declared himself Patron and Founder, they were to be joined by some of the highest officers of his court and of the Anglican Church; for by then the Society had become fashionable.

"The Ballad of Gresham Colledge"

The activities of these Original Fellows in those first months can be gleaned not only from their carefully kept minutes but also from a contemporary ballad that happens to have survived to this day. These doggerel verses, by internal evidence apparently composed before 1663, were evidently passed around, for at least three manuscript copies have been preserved in the British Museum.[3]

3 Since this section was written, Mr. F. Sherwood Taylor has published "An Early Satirical Poem on the Royal Society" (*Notes and Records of the Royal Society in London,* October, 1947, pp. 37-46) based on a fourth manuscript in the British Museum and on two others in the Ashmolean collection at Oxford. (See below, p. 254.)

One copy has names written in the margins identifying the people spoken of, and another gives the author as "Mr. W. Glanvill." That seems perhaps a mistake for the better known Joseph Glanvill whose *Vanity of Dogmatizing* had already appeared and who was whole-heartedly one of the virtuosi himself, becoming a Fellow in 1664. But whoever wrote them, the author of the verses was familiar with the purposes of the Society and with their experiments, for he gives a fairly accurate account of some of their early interests and achievements. As this ballad seems to be the only one of this early period in the Society's history that has come down to our time, it is given here in full, together with the marginal identifications from one of the manuscripts.

In Praise of that choice Company of Witts and Philosophers who meet on Wednesdays weekly att Gresham Colledg.

If to be rich and to be learn'd
Be every Nation's cheifest glory
How much are English men concern'd,
Gresham, to celebrate thy story
Who built th'Exchange t'enrich the Citty
And a Colledge founded for the witty.

II

Our Merchants on th'Exchange doe plott
T'increase the Kingdom's wealth by trade.
Att Gresham Colledge a learned Knott
Unparallel'd designes have laid
To make themselves a Corporation
And knowe all things by Demonstration.

III

Seaven was the number of the Sages;
The eight wiseman wee call a Foole.

Our Fame must then exceed all Ages
Who have Seaventie wise men in one Schoole.
Wee adore the, Gresham, for thy Colledge
From whence must issue soe much Knowledg.

IV

This learned Septuagint consists
Of men of Honor and of parts.
There's L[or]ds, K[nigh]ts, Physicians, Priests
All skill'd in Sciences and Arts
Solomons in nature and can read there
Even from the Hysop to the Cedar.

V

Thy Colledg, Gresham, shall hereafter
Be the whole world's Universitie.
Oxford and Cambridge are our laughter;
Their learning is but Pedantry.
These new Collegiates doe assure us
Aristotle's an Asse to Epicurus.

VI

By demonstrative Philosophie
They playnly prove all things are bodyes,
And those that talke of Qualitie
They count them all to be meer Noddyes.
Nature in all her works they trace
And make her as playne as nose in face.

VII

'Twas broach't att first but to make myrth
There was another world i' th' Moone: MR. WILKINS
The Colledg proves that Globe an Earth
And Made 't as playne as day att Noone,
Nay, in a glasse of Fiftie Foot   SIR P. NEALE
They shew us Rivers and Trees to boot.

VIII

To the Danish Agent late was showne
That where noe Ayre is, there's noe breath.
A glasse this secret did make knowne   MR. BOYLE
Where[in] a Catt was put to death.
Out of the glasse the Ayre being screwed
Pusse dyed and ne're so much as mewed.

IX

The selfe same glasses did likewise clear
Another secret more profound:
That nought but Ayre unto the Eare
Can be the Medium of Sound,
For in the glasse emptied of Ayre
A striking watch you cannot heare.

X

And that which makes their Fame ring louder
With much adoe they shew'd the King
To make glasse Buttons turn to powder,
If off the[m] their tayles you doe but wring.
How this was donne by soe small Force
Did cost the Colledg a Month's discourse.

XI

These men take nothing uppon trust
Therefor in Counsell sate many howres
About fileing Iron into Dust
T'experiment the Loadstone's powers;
If in a Circle of a Board they strew it,
By what lines to see the Loadstone drew it.

XII

The noble learned Corporation
Not for itselfe is thus combyn'd
But for the publique good oth'Nation
And generall benefitt of Mankynd.

59

These are not men of common mould:
They covet Fame but contemne gold.

XIII

But yett they'd have the Colledge endow'd
With about a thousand pounds a year.
Such a Revenue being allow'd
What things they'll doe shall then appeare.
Each single Member hath undertooke
To shew a Trick or write a Booke.

XIV

The Prime Virtuoso hath undertaken
Through all the Experiments to run   SIR R[OBERT] M[ORAY]
Of that learned Man, Sir Francis Bacon,
Shewing which can, which can't, be donne.
If he doe not, be sure that none
Will ever fynd the Philosopher's stone.

XV

A second hath describ'd att full   SIR W[ILLIA]M P[ETTY]
The Philosophie of making Cloath,
Tells you what grasse doth make coarse wooll
And whatt it is that breeds the Moth.
Great learning is i'th' Art of Cloathing
Though vulgar people thinke it nothing.

XVI

A wondrous Engine is contriveing
In forme, 'tis said, much like a Bell,
Most usefull for the Art of Diveing
If't hitt, 'twill prove a Miracle:
For, gentlemen, 'tis no small matter,
To make a man breath under water.

60

XVII

A new designe how to make Leather
A third Collegiate is now scaning.　　MR. [CHARLES] HOW[ARD]
The Question most disputed: wheather
Since without Barke there may be taning,
Some cheaper way may not be tryed
Of makeing Leather without Hyde.

XVIII

Another person of great noate　　　SIR K[ENELM] DIGBY
Hath writt a Learned tract of Strawe
The tallest Beane stalke and smallest moate
From their first principles to drawe.
A fifth writes that in no tyne shorter
Then twen[t]y yeers can be made good Morter.

XIX

A sixth is perfecting a treatise
Of Draweing, Paynting, Lymning, graveing,—
A most Ingenious peece, some say 'tis,
And wilbe richly worth men's haveing
For it declares the very Prime Age
Either of Painter or of Image.

XX

It proves that Aaron, the Jewes' high Priest,—
A controversie worth the cleering,—
Must fall within the sculpture's List;
When he mad Golden Calfe of Eare Ring,
He needs must use a toole of Mould
For fire could never shape the gold.

XXI

A Doctor counted very able
Designes that all Mankynd converse shall,
Spite o'th' confusion made att Babell,
By Character call'd Universall.

61

How long this Character will be learning,
That truly passeth my discerning.

XXII

To guesse by one every one's meritt,   MR. EVEL[YN]
A Booke call'd Fumifugiam read.
Its Author hath a publique Spirit
And doubtlesse too a subtile head;
He must be more than John an Oake
Who writes soe learnedly of Smoake.

XXIII

He shewes that 'tis the seacoale smoake
That allways London doth Inviron,
Which doth our Lungs and Spiritts choake
Our hangings spoyle, and rust our Iron.
Lett none att Fumifuge be scoffing
Who heare att Church our Sundaye's Coughing.

XXIV

For melioration of the Ayre
Both for our Lungs and eke our noses
To plant the Fields he doth take care
With Cedar, Juniper and Roses,
Which, turn'd to trees, 'tis understood
Wee shall instead of coale burne wood.

XXV

O blessed witt that thus contrives
By new found out but facile Arte
In pleasure to lengthen out our lives,
To teach us next to perfume ———,
And without fuell or smoake make fire
Some other Member will aspire.

XXVI

The Colledge will the whole world measure,
Which most impossible conclude,
And Navigation make a pleasure
By fynding out the Longitude.
Every Tarpaulin shall then with ease
Sayle any ship to the Antipodes.

XXVII

Of all the Arts Mechanicall
Printed shalbe a perfe[ct] Scheme,
And every Science Liberall
Shall be likewise a Colledge Theame.
When the King hath made them a Societie
They'll demonstrate all things but a Dietie.

XXVIII

These be the things with many more
Which miraculous appere to men
The Colledge intended: The like before
Were never donne, nor wilbe agen.
And to conclude in Ballad Fashion
God blesse the King and this new Corporation.

Thus the Royal Society by the end of 1663 had its charter, its membership list, its governing body, and a wide-ranging program in action, as well as a name, a coat of arms with a motto, and a mace. On November 30, 1663, it held its first anniversary meeting for the election of officers for the next year. November 30th happens to be St. Andrew's day, the patron saint of Scotland. Why this day should have been chosen for the annual meeting instead of November 28th when the agreement was actually drawn up is not known. Possibly it was out of compliment to the Scot, Sir Robert Moray, who had been most instrumental in securing the King's favor and in getting the charters. Anyway, John Aubrey, one of the Original Fellows, has left a note of a conversation with another Fellow, Sir William Petty, who had been one of the virtuosi at least from the early Oxford days. "I remember," Aubrey wrote, "one St. Andrew's Day (which is the day of the generall meeting of the Royall Society for annual elections). I says, 'Methought 'twas not so well we should pitch upon the Patron Saint of Scotland's Day; we should rather have St. George or St. Isidore (a philosopher canonized).' 'No,' says Sir William, 'I had rather have had it been on St. Thomas's Day, for he would not beleeve till he had seen and putt his fingers into the holes; according to the motto, "Nullius in verba" '."

That motto from Horace was, the official *Record of the Royal Society* states, "an expression of their (the Society's) determination to withstand the domination of authority and to verify all statements by an appeal to facts." It was the one they had chosen, at Evelyn's suggestion, to have emblazoned on the coat of arms granted them in the second charter.

Early Difficulties

Questions of finance plagued the Fellows from the first. Despite Charles' patronage and his gift of the mace, he granted them no government subsidy. This was in marked contrast to royal practice at the time on the continent. In France, Colbert, the great minister under Louis XIV, founded the *Académie des Sciences* in 1666 practically as an arm of the government with its members appointed and paid by Colbert, its work subsidized by the state and its publications during its first years printed as the work of the *Académie* rather than as the work of individual members. The scientific societies that spread rapidly in the next decades through the courts of Europe followed the French model in being subsidized by the state, rather than the English one of governmental favor and private support.

The Royal Society in England had to struggle along on

the funds supplied by its members as admission fees and as weekly dues. Many of the Fellows let the payment of their weekly shillings fall in arrears, and the officers hoped eagerly for help from the King. First there was talk of a grant of some of the confiscated estates in Ireland. Then in 1669 came the royal gift of the Chelsea College lands, but Charles bought them back some years later for other purposes, and the Society continued to limp along with a heavy debt of unpaid dues and with few gifts and bequests to relieve the financial strain.

Henry Oldenburg, one of the two first secretaries elected (the other was Dr. Wilkins), complained bitterly about the burden of work the Society gave him and about his need for money to reimburse him. An intelligencer or news-distributor like his friend Hartlib, Oldenburg first visited England in 1640 for eight years. Then, after some years on the continent, he had returned to London in 1653 as an agent for the city of Bremen, near which he had been born and in which he had been educated. He came again the next year, then stayed on, serving as a tutor to sons of the nobility, Boyle's nephew among others, and traveling with them abroad. Upon his return to London in 1660 he joined the Royal Society in December while it was in process of organization, and was elected one of the two first secretaries. Later, with Robert Hooke as its first "curator," he became one of the two first salaried officers, to be joined in 1672 by a third, Dr. Nehemiah Grew, the noted plant anatomist. From 1660 till his death in 1677, Oldenburg devoted himself to his work as an intelligencer of scientific news, working especially for and with Boyle, and also from 1665 on, as editor of the *Philosophical Transactions*.

The Philosophical Transactions *and Oldenburg*

Phil. Trans., as it is often spoken of familiarly, is the oldest scientific journal in the English-speaking world, and missed by three months being the oldest of all. It was first issued in March, 1665; but the *Journal des Savans* of the French academicians had first appeared that January, just three months earlier. The English journal was an outgrowth of Oldenburg's work as secretary and reporter of Royal Society affairs, founded and financed by him as a means of personal profit if possible, but with the authorization of the Society back of him. He had had so many inquiries to answer from correspondents abroad and at home who wanted to know about the Society's work and about scientific news generally that it seemed simpler to him to print a monthly report, and by its sale to get some return for all the work he was doing for the Society.

A publication like this would have the especial advantage of recording priority of discovery. As he wrote Boyle that year (Aug. 29, 1665), "I acknowledge that that jealousy about the first authors of experiments which you speak of, is not groundless; and therefore offer myself to register all those you, or any person, shall please to communicate as new, with that fidelity, which both the honour of my relation to the Royal Society (which is highly concerned in such experiments) and my own inclinations, do strongly oblige me to."

Quarrels about priority raged bitterly in those days. Codes of ethics among authors as well as inventors were notably absent. Writers took what they wanted from other men's books and there were many complaints about the stealing of men's ideas and inventions. In fact, one way Oldenburg served Boyle whose sight was poor, making him dependent on secretarial help, was by storing for him "notes and other loose papers" which were not to be shown to others without Boyle's permission. Oldenburg also once wrote Boyle (Nov. 5, 1664) that he had sent Boyle's manuscripts to a printer who would "keep them unexposed to the eye of a philosophical robber."

However, Christopher Wren's biographers, his son and his grandson, complained later that "Sir Christopher has been heard sometimes to reflect sharply on the disingenuity of Mr. Oldenburg who had neglected not only to enter divers inventions and experiments of his in the Registers of the Society, but conveyed the same into foreign parts, France and Germany; where they were after published under other names, as their own." Sprat, too, complained that the early records were incomplete about Wren's work, "many excellent things, whose first invention ought to be ascribed to him (Wren)" having been "casually omitted." At least the *Philosophical Transactions* was available to render a major service when it was properly used.

With its publication Oldenburg was not out of his financial troubles. Rather, his difficulties grew worse. The great plague of 1665 seemed peculiarly fatal to printers, and the Oxford printers whom he had had to use temporarily paid him less than half the revenue he had expected from the sale of his monthly. In September, 1666, came the terrible Fire of London, destroying all the copies of the *Transactions* which had not yet been sold, as well as greatly increasing his own expenses and lessening his expected income from publication. That December the Society granted him a salary of £40.

Finally, in June 1667, Oldenburg found himself a prisoner in the Tower of London "for dangerous designs and practices." His heavy foreign correspondence evidently appeared suspicious to the authorities. On June 25th, Samuel Pepys wrote in his diary: "I was told yesterday that Mr. Oldenburg, our secretary at Gresham College [Pepys means, of the Royal Society that meets at Gresham College] is put into the Tower, for writing newes to a virtuoso in France, with whom he constantly corresponds in philosophical matters; which makes it very unsafe at this time to write, or almost do anything."

Evelyn, the other great diarist, wrote on the 8th of August that he had visited Mr. Oldenburg, "now close prisoner in the Tower, being suspected of writing intelligence," and added, "I am confident he will prove an innocent person." So it was. Oldenburg was released on August 26th and a week later he wrote Boyle: "I was so stifled by the prison air, that as soon as I had my enlargement from the Tower, I widened it and took it from London into the country to fan myself for some days in the good air of Craford in Kent. Being now returned and having recovered my stomach which I had in a manner quite lost, I intend if God will, to fall to my old trade if I have support to follow it. My late misfortune, I fear, will much prejudice me; many persons unacquainted with me, and hearing me to be a stranger [alien], being apt to derive a suspicion upon me. Not a few came to the Tower merely to enquire after my crime, and to see the warrant; in which, when they found it was for dangerous designs and practices, they spread it over London, and made others have no good opinion of me."

Even more serious was the shutting down of his correspondents' activities following his imprisonment. The letters on which he depended for his news did not come, which made him "conjecture that foreigners especially in the neighboring parts, may be grown shy to resume that commerce they were wont to entertain with me, out of some tenderness and concern for my safety, which they may judge may be endangered as well by their freeness in writing to me as by mine of writing to them."

Oldenburg persevered, however, and by the end of 1667 (December 17) was "groaning" over the work. "I have no less at present, than 30 correspondents, partly domestick, partly foreign. Many of them I not only write to, but also do business for; which requires much time to enquire after such particulars and despatch such business as they desire if I mean to be gratified reciprocally in such things as I bespeak of them. Besides my constant attendance on the meetings of the Society and Council and preserving what is said and done there, and giving order to have all registered and reviewing all the entries; soliciting also the performances of the manifold tasks recommended and undertaken by the members of the Society; and distributing and sending them abroad such directions and enquiries, as are thought conducive to advance our design, etc., I confess I extend my patience as far as I can."

On the last day of March, 1668, he wrote again: "The fame of the Society riseth very high abroad; and makes strangers flock hither in troops; insomuch that since this March I have had no less than two dozen travellers addressed to me, whereof some make quick dispatch, others stay longer." Two years later the Society increased his salary, but he still had to supplement his income by the translation of books into Latin.

Oldenburg continued as editor of the *Philosophical Transactions* as long as he lived, issuing 136 numbers and writing or translating 34 of the articles in them. Papers read before the Society, letters, summaries and abstracts of books of special interest to the virtuosi,—the scientific news of the day was summed up in this journal. After his death in 1677, the journal was continued under the secretaries' private editorship through 46 volumes with only limited supervision by the Society. For a brief while, during Hooke's editorship it was called the *Philosophical Collections* (1679-82), and once for a period of three years (1688-90) it was not issued at all. Finally, with the 47th volume in 1752, the *Transactions* was taken over by the Society and published by its Committee on Papers. The intelligencers of the seventeenth century had at last given way to the editors of the eighteenth century.

Oldenburg was not a scientist himself; he was the friend and correspondent of science-lovers, for whom he served as an intermediary. He had a small but active part in fertilizing the soil and watering the ground out of which grew the work of the true scientists. He was one of the key men during the first formative years of the Royal Society and he founded its great publication, the *Philosophical Transactions*. His work, and that of others like him both in and out of the Society, helped to make the seventeenth century outstanding for its major contributions to the development of modern science.

5

EARLY OPPOSITION TO THE ROYAL SOCIETY

TO JUDGE the worth of an institution and of its
activities, one should consider the statements of its
critics as well as those of its friends. That the critics
of the Royal Society were influential as well as numerous
and vociferous during its formative years is apparent at
once. Otherwise why should an institution hardly five years
old have an official history written? Yet that is what Thomas
Sprat's *History of the Royal Society* is in name, though the
author admitted it was an apology or defense rather than a
history. Possibly the imprisonment of Oldenburg, the secretary, in 1667 shortly before the *History* was published,
gave added urgency for an official presentation of its case.

The Society had a number of difficulties with which to
contend. The members were not paying their dues
promptly and the total in arrears was mounting rapidly.
To outsiders their activities seemed both futile in themselves and also dangerous to the state and to the estab-

lished church. They were thought dangerous too in their daring disregard for ancient learning and time-honored authority. Of course jealousy of the fashionable young Society was a factor also. The critics were keen and their ridicule sharp. No one enjoys being laughed at.

Sprat's Defense of the Society

Therefore Sprat presented his case in favor of the virtuosi with all the eloquence at his command. His book is in three parts. First, after a short review of ancient philosophy with an appreciation of the syllogistic reasoning of the middle ages, he pleaded for an improvement over the past as well as for a return to what he called the true past when men really studied and observed nature's ways. Thus he tried to meet the arguments of the traditionalists who objected to the novelty of the "new philosophy" that Francis Bacon had so brilliantly supported.

In the second part Sprat narrated the origins of the Society, stressing as he did so the influence of Cowley's proposed "philosophical college," a suggestion published just at the time that the virtuosi were making plans for their organization. Besides being a friend of Sprat, Cowley was a well-known Royalist. Might not Sprat have emphasized his friend's scheme both for its own sake and also because of its author's political orthodoxy in those early Restoration days when the Cromwellian blight and the Puritan cast of thought still marked the recent background of a number of the virtuosi? [1] Was it not a subtle and discreet indication that the Society had Royalist as well as Puritan roots and so would not be dangerous to the re-established regime?

After discussing Cowley's plan as too costly to be practicable but as wisely placing great importance on education, Sprat concluded that the Society was putting most of his proposals into effect. He then went on to describe

1 Raven, C. E. *John Ray, Naturalist* (Cambridge, 1942) 145-6 and note.

the new organization and its membership with illustrations of the types of work being done and of the various
individuals doing it. Here he was meeting the arguments
of those who considered the work frivolous and laughable,
and who held that the Fellows demeaned themselves in
associating with craftsmen and artisans, practical men who
were not "gentlemen scholars." Among the Fellows whose
work he selected as illustrations were Sir William Petty,
Robert Hooke, Lawrence Rooke, and especially Christopher Wren. Posterity has only recently begun fully to
appreciate and understand his choice of Wren. Christopher Wren, not long ago referred to by an eminent English historian as "probably the greatest Englishman since
Shakespeare" [2] has been obscured as a scientist by his fame
as the architect of London after the Great Fire. St. Paul's
Cathedral has stood so long as the monument to his architectural genius, together with some fifty London churches,
that not many have realized fully the universality of his
genius. Sprat might well consider that he and these other
men, by their personal character, their social standing,
and their already great scientific achievements should stop
the mouths of the critics and still the scoffers. But as will be
seen, Sprat did not succeed. The wits continued to belabor
the Society and its activities for many years to come.

In the third part of his *History* Sprat defended the Society and its activities against the charge of atheism, and
pointed to the bishops and other clergy who were active
in the Society as living proof that it was no threat to religion nor to the established church, but on the contrary
was a supremely worthwhile activity, in keeping with the
true temper of that age and for its best interests.

Taken as a whole, the main theme of the *History* is an
enthusiastic support of experiment and observation as the
basis for the advancement of learning. It places the emphasis upon nature rather than upon books, upon objects
rather than theories, and upon the importance of assem-

[2] H. A. L. Fisher, Nov. 8, 1929, cited by John F. Fulton. The Rise of the
Experimental Method. *Yale Jour. of Biol. & Med.* March 1931, p. 315.

bling data by cooperative enterprise rather than by single-handed effort. Thus knowledge would be furthered, and comfort and convenience as well.

Sprat the Author

Thomas Sprat himself was not a scientist nor apparently even an amateur of science, for all his support of the "new philosophy." He was a man of letters and a friend and fellow-student of many of the virtuosi. He was elected a Fellow in 1663 along with a number of other notables in London society. He had been at Wadham College in Oxford under Warden Wilkins, matriculating there in 1651, receiving his B.A. in 1654, his M.A. in 1657, and a fellowship at the College immediately thereafter. He was ordained to the priesthood of the Anglican Church at the time of the Restoration, and through his friendship with Cowley, the poet, became chaplain to the Duke of Buckingham. Sprat received his B.D. and his D.D. in 1669, resigning his fellowship at Wadham the following year. He became chaplain to Charles II, then dean of Westminster Abbey, and ultimately bishop of Rochester for nineteen years before his death in 1713. Both at Wadham College and in London he had been in the midst of the virtuosi, "turning about" with many of them from moderate support of Puritan and Cromwellian affairs to acceptance of the Stuart line and of the established church. Thereafter he was a churchman and later a Tory. After his *History* was published, scientific matters apparently concerned him little, if at all.

Sprat's reputation as a wit was great and he had already had occasion to rise to the defense of the Society. He had been annoyed by Mons. Samuel Sorbière's *Rélation* in 1664 of a journey he had made to England shortly before. Through Oldenburg, whom he had met when he was in Paris with Boyle's nephew, and Sir Robert Moray, Sorbière had been presented to the King in England and had also attended meetings of the Royal Society. As he did not understand English, Sir Robert had sat beside him and acted as interpreter.

Sorbière's comments on what he saw at the court and at these meetings reflected the somewhat amused detachment with which the educated regarded the virtuosi's enthusiasms. He considered it a most edifying sight to see so prominent a nobleman as Sir Robert himself adjusting telescopes and setting up experiments. Such activities, Sorbière understood, had been taken up by people of quality during the exile of the King and in the absence of the court. Even the King himself, he related, had found consolation in these occupations during his exile, and still continued his interest, having brought a chemist over from Paris and having had a laboratory built for him at St. James' Park. But the King's greatest interest lay in the problems of navigation about which, in Sorbière's opinion, he had a remarkable understanding. That special interest was to bear fruit later on in the founding of the Royal Observatory.

The Royal Society particularly impressed Sorbière by the range and usefulness of its activities and also by the conduct of its meetings. He found the rooms at Gresham College convenient and spacious and the meetings themselves orderly and direct. No one interrupted. Disagreements were not pushed, nor made in a disagreeable tone of voice. The debates could not be more civil, more respectful, nor better conducted. If anyone talked to his neighbor he whispered, and stopped instantly at the president's rap of his little gavel, so no one failed to hear what was said. Sorbière was so much impressed (or did he wish to be in the fashion?) that he joined the Society himself in 1663 and signed the charter book. After his book had appeared, however, the Society debated whether to eject him or not; but a majority of the Fellows voted in his favor.

Sprat did not think that the Frenchman had done full justice to the Society and said so in some *Observations* he printed in 1665 as a letter to Wren. He protested that Sorbière had made the meetings appear like the sessions of a school and he denounced in no uncertain terms Sorbière's reference to the beginnings of a library, saying that the Society had none, for it had no intention of having a "Professorian Philosophy." . . . "With Books they meddle not farther than to see what Experiments have been try'd before; their Revenue they designe for Operators and not for Lecturers." Sprat pointed out also that Sorbière had confused the Society with Gresham College, a totally different institution, though the Society was meeting in the College buildings.

It is not surprising, therefore, that when the virtuosi wanted a full account of their Society presented in answer to the rising criticisms of it, they turned to Sprat who had already spoken out in their defense. With their official sanction and assistance he wrote the *History* for them. This was his main service to the Society,—and to English literature.

Sprat well knew that the conservatives of his time, who were particularly well entrenched in the universities, were staunch supporters of medieval Aristotelianism. Aristotle had written on almost every subject,—on nature, on the soul, on plants, and on politics, on astronomy, and on the generation of animals, to name but a few,—and he had spoken with an authority upheld by men of learning for centuries upon centuries. At the beginning of the seventeenth century, as has already been pointed out, Francis Bacon had done his best in all his books to shake that dominance which the Aristotelian philosophy still retained over men's minds. So Sprat, giving full credit to Bacon's influence as the inspiration of the Royal Society's work, asserted that the Fellows were showing no disrespect to Aristotle and to other ancient authorities in making further explorations of the natural world and in testing the truth or falsity of what they had already declared. But the supporters of the ancients continued to think otherwise, nor did Sprat succeed in shutting off the attacks along this line. This quarrel between the ancients and the moderns raged on vigorously during the remainder of the century not only in science but also in literature—"the battle of the books" as it came to be called.

The Microscope and Divine Works

In dealing with the supposed antagonism of the "new philosophy" for that other "authority," that of the established church and of religion itself, Sprat not only countered with the numbers of active Fellows who were divines and even bishops, like Dr. Wilkins and Seth Ward, the Bishop of Exeter, but he also emphasized the revelation of God the Creator as seen through the study of His handiwork even in the minutest objects of the natural world. The authority of the Bible and of the church was not shaken, he claimed, rather it was strengthened by such evidence as Robert Hooke had uncovered with the recently developed compound microscope. In emphasizing these discoveries, little could Sprat have realized what excellent ammunition they would provide for the attacks on the Society by the wits and the satirists in the years to come.

Even before the Society had received its first Charter, Robert Hooke, Boyle's assistant at Oxford, had been appointed curator of the Society's experiments, on Boyle's recommendation, and had been included as one of the Original Fellows. He had published his classic *Micrographia* in 1665 on his researches with the first compound microscopes. His drawings of the eye of a fly, of a hair, of a bit of cloth, of seeds as magnified by these lenses had captivated the virtuosi, and observations with the microscope were often made at the early meetings of the Society. Christopher Wren, while at Oxford with Wilkins at Wadham College, had already done some of this work, improving the microscope mechanically, and with his mathematical genius finding how to calculate the magnification of the object under the lens. Some of Wren's drawings of what

76

he had seen thereby, a louse, a flea, a nit, were already in the King's collection of rarities. Charles wanted more of these "divine works," Sprat wrote to Wren. Instead, Wren asked release from this request and encouraged Hooke to go on with the experiments. The *Micrographia* resulted. Sprat held that the revelation of such perfection in the tiniest of objects, far from lessening one's faith, strengthened and increased it.

Such activities, however, were just what the wits of the day jumped at. "They [the virtuosi] can admire nothing except fleas, lice and themselves," declared Dr. South, the university orator at Oxford.[3] The occasion of this outburst was the dedication on July 9, 1669 of the Sheldonian theater given to the university as an auditorium for great occasions by Archbishop Sheldon and designed by Christopher Wren. Presumably many of the virtuosi were present there that day. Dr. John Wallis describing the festivities to Robert Boyle in a letter later that month wrote: "Dr. South as university orator made a long oration. The first part of which consisted of satyrical invectives against Cromwell, fanaticks, the Royal Society and new philosophy; the next of encomiasticks in praise of the archbishop, the theater, the vice chancellor, the architect and the painter; the last of execrations against fanaticks, conventicles, comprehension and new philosophy; damning them *ad inferos, ad gehennam* (to hell, to Gehenna)." Evelyn also was present and recorded that "Dr. South, the University Orator, made an eloquent speech, which was very long, and not without some malicious and indecent reflections on the Royal Society, as underminers of the University, which was very foolish and untrue, as well as unseasonable."

3 I. D'Israeli quoted this sentence in the early nineteenth century as though he had read the speech itself. It is a matter of great regret that prolonged search in 1930 failed to unearth this oration.

Charles II and the Society

Meantime others besides Sorbière came to visit the meetings of the Society: royalty, foreigners, a great court lady even. Charles II was genuinely interested in the new science and in the work of the Society of which he was Founder and Patron. When he let it be known he wished to visit a session, preparations were most carefully considered. Lord Brouncker, the president, wrote to Wren in Oxford asking for his suggestions for suitable experiments to be presented. Wren's long letter in reply was full of good sense. The experiments to be shown "should open new light into principles of philosophy" and yet "whose use and advantage is obvious, and without a lecture, and besides may surprize with some unexpected effect and be commendable for the ingenuity of the contrivance." Wren went on to consider the difficulties of various types of demonstrations for such an occasion, as for example, "Experiments in anatomy, though of the most value for their use, are sordid and noisome to any but those whose desire of knowledge makes them digest it." Finally he suggested from among his own devices, "the weather-wheel (the only true way to measure expansion of the air)," an artificial eye "at least as big as a tennis ball," and a "needle that would play in a coach" [a kind of compass] joined with a "way-wiser" [an odometer or roadmeasurer] as both useful and diverting to a traveler and as an acceptable present for the King.

The Council itself on July 6, 1663, made plans for the King's entertainment at a meeting a week later. Mr. Hooke and the operator (or technician) were to take care that the compressing engine would not fail that day. Various Fellows were to have on display their personal collections of rarities; Dr. Ent was to prepare a dissection of an oyster or a lobster; Wren was to suggest some experiments and Dr. Wilkins was requested "to undertake the experiment of raising a great weight by a man's breath;

and that of a metallic tree, both with mercury, after Dr. Power's way, red and green, and to engage Dr. Power to do magnetic experiments." Dr. Goddard also was to make some experiments. There is unfortunately no clear record whether or not the King ever actually came to a session of the Society.

Wilkins' own report on his type of experiment is still among the manuscripts of the Royal Society and in itself forms an interesting illustration of the Society's struggles with laboratory work and of the way these early experiments were reported. Any one who has ever had to write up a laboratory report of any sort according to the exacting standards of modern science might be interested in seeing how a report was made for the files less than three hundred years ago. In modern terms, Dr. Wilkins was investigating the effects of compressing air through tubes of small caliber. Similar weight lifting is now used in tests of lung capacity. (See Plate 11.)

Experiments concerning the Force of Blowing
        with a man's Breath   Read July 31,61
        By Dr. Wilkins   Ent'd. R.B. 1.57

Take the Bladder of an Oxe or Cow. Fasten to the neck of it a pipe of about a Quarter of an inch bore and 6 or 8 inches long. Let one end of the pipe be trumpet fashion, for the more convenient applying of the lippe to it. If the whole body of this Bladder to that very end where 'tis fastened to the pipe, be layde flatt upon a table (All the Aire being first thrust out) then a joint stoole turned upside downe, being set upon the bladder, and a footeboy of about 16 or 17 yeares old sitting on the other end of the joynt stoole: A man may by blowing this Bladder lift up the stoole and boy about 2 Inches.*

* My attention has been called by Miss Edith Bruce Paterson to a similar experiment appearing in a textbook published in 1942 for use in junior high school classes in physics. In this experiment, a board about six feet long is used instead of a box. For the bladder a football is substituted into which compressed air is forced by a bicycle pump. If one end of the board is placed on the empty football and a pupil stands on the board near that end, air forced into the ball will lift the pupil a few inches. (Clarke, J. A., Fitzpatrick, F. L., and Smith, E. L., *Science on the March*, Boston, 1942, 78-9.)

Let a string be fastened to the lower end of the Bladder, the other end of it being tyed to a Chaire or stoole lying upon a Table, a little beyond the edge of the Table. Let the other end of the string which hangs down, be fastnd to a Weight on the Ground (suppose of 50 or a hundred pound). Let the string be so tyed betwixt the bottom of the Bladder, and the Ring of the Weight that it may be pretty tense and not Laxe. Then if one blowe into the Bladder, as that doth extend and shorten, the Weight will rise from the Ground about 3 or 4 Inches.

If a Square boxe be made, open at one end, with a hole at the bottom or other end, to put through the neck of the bladder and the pipe, Each corner of this bottom having a legg of about 2 or 3 inches long to keep it of[f] from the table. Let the empty bladder be equally tyed at the bottom of this boxe. Then lay upon the bladder thus tyed a Square borde that may move easily within the hollow of the Boxe. Upon this borde sett 110 lb. weight, or somewhat more. Then blowing at the pipe, this weight will ascend about 5 or 6 Inches.

Note: If the Bore of the Pipe be much lesse, like that at the small end of a tobacco pipe, a man will not be able to stirre this Weight so that it would seeme that there is a certaine proportion to be observed in the Bore of the Pipe beyond or short of which, the blowing of the same man will not be of the same force.

Quaere. Whether this proportion be not answerable to that of the Aqua Salienter.

King Charles, for all his interest in the Royal Society, loved a good joke. He "mightily laughed at Gresham College," Pepys reported on February 1, 1663/4, "for spending time only in weighing of ayre and doing nothing else since they sat." One wonders if the King didn't have his tongue in his cheek when he sent his query to the Society asking "why sensitive plants stir and contract themselves upon being touched." A committee of five, including Wilkins, Evelyn, and Boyle, was appointed on July 17, 1661, "for examining the fact relating to these plants"; but their report, if they made one, was not recorded. Previously he had sent them two "loadstones" or magnets with the re-

PLATE 8. The Mace given to the Royal Society by Charles II, Founder and Patron of the Society

(From *The Record of the Royal Society*, London, 1940, by courtesy of the Royal Society)

PLATE 9. Henry Oldenburg

(From *The Record of the Royal Society*, London, 1940, by courtesy of the Royal Society)

quest that they send him accounts of any considerable experiments made with them.

A few months before he had sent them five little glass bubbles, two with liquor in them and the other three solid, to get the Society's judgment on them. The Society spent some time that summer in getting more glass bubbles made and in experimenting with them. Finally the minutes for August 14 record a full report, stating among other facts: "A blow with a small hammer . . . will not break one of the glass drops made in water, if it be touched no where but upon the body. Break off the top of it and it will fly immediately into very minute parts with a smart force and noise; and these parts will easily crumble into a coarse dust." In his *Micrographia* in 1665 Hooke also reported on some of the phenomena of these glass drops.

The King's brother, visitors from abroad, and various ambassadors and foreign agents resident in London were not the only guests who came with curious interest and, some of them, accepted membership in the Society. Londoners and science-lovers from other English cities coming to the capital also wanted to see for themselves some of the amazing experiments about which there was talk. Perhaps their appetites were whetted by the current ballads and the jokes and also by the literary controversies already stirring. One of the younger virtuosi, Joseph Glanvill, soon to be elected a Fellow, had written a highly enthusiastic book (*The Vanity of Dogmatizing*, 1661) about the many marvels that might soon be expected from this "new philosophy." He was shortly to be challenged by one of the Society's bitterest critics, Dr. Henry Stubbs. Sprat in his *History* again and again refers to the jibes of such critics which made him produce an apology or defense rather than a historian's record.

The Visit of the Duchess of Newcastle

One of these important visitors whose request for an invitation to a meeting of the Royal Society created considerable stir was Margaret Cavendish, Duchess of Newcastle. She was making one of her rare visits to London in the spring of 1667 and was attracting great attention wherever she went; for she was remarkably "wise, witty and learned" [4] and also remarkably eccentric. "Mad Madge," she was called, and a sight she must have been as she drove through the London streets with her coach, her horses, her attendants and herself all in the black and silver she affected. Pepys remarked that May he could not get near her in the streets to see how she looked because of the crowd of boys and girls running after her coach, and on another occasion because of the people in coaches who followed and crowded on her wherever she went. When she asked to come to the Royal Society, the members debated long before they invited her; for, as Pepys recorded, "we do believe the town will be full of ballads of it."

The Duchess finally came on May 30, 1667, and a very large crowd assembled to welcome her; but Pepys was not impressed. "Anon comes the Duchesse with her women attending her. . . . The Duchesse hath been a good comely woman; but her dress so antick and her deportment so ordinary, that I do not like her at all, nor did I hear her say anything that was worth hearing, but that she was full of admiration. Several fine experiments were shown her, of colours, loadstones, microscopes and of liquors: among others, of one that did, while she was there, turn a piece of roasted mutton into pure blood, which was very rare . . . After they had shown her many experiments, and she cried still she was full of admiration, she departed, being led out and in by several Lords that were there . . ." (One wonders how Pepys would have voted in 1945 when two

[4] Her epitaph, cited by B. G. MacCarthy, *Women Writers, Their Contribution to the English Novel, 1621–1744* (Cork University, 1944) 91.

distinguished women scientists were proposed as Fellows!)

The minutes of the Council for May 23, 1667, list the experiments planned for her entertainment, while the Society's minutes give those actually performed. The Council selected experiments with "1. Colours, 2. The mixing of cold liquors, which upon their infusion grew hot, 3. The swimming of bodies in the midst of water, 4. The dissolving of meat in the oil of vitriol, 5. The weighing of air in a receiver, by means of the rarefying engine, 6. The marbles exactly flatted, 7. The magnet, and in particular that of a terrella [a spherical magnet] driving away the steel-dust at its poles, 8. A good microscope. These experiments Mr. Boyle and Mr. Hooke were desired to provide and take care of." Of these they weighed the air. They showed several experiments on mixing colors, and one on mixing two cold liquors which then became hot. They tried drawing water into the rarefying machine. They tested "a body swimming in water" and finally they sought to pull apart "two well wrought marbles which were not separated but by the weight of 47 pounds."

Pepys' opinion of the Duchess is hardly fair to her, however closely he reflected the opinion of his age that she was queer. Another story about her, whether apocryphal or not, reflects that same contemporary opinion. One day at court she was talking to Dr. Wilkins, then Bishop of Chester, about his schemes for journeying to the moon and asked, if the trip took 180 days, where would he bait [feed] his horses on the way. He expressed surprise that she should be the one to ask that question, she "who had built so many castles in the air, she might lie every night in one of her own." [5]

Modern scholars claim she had sufficient genius to justify her eccentricity even though lack of education rendered her intellectual powers ineffectual. After reviewing her books a recent critic sums up the Duchess in the following sentence: "Her genius was so productive and so various,

[5] Daniel Neal, *History of the Puritans*, ed. by Toulmin (5 vols. London, 1822) III, 393 n.

her ideas so original and ill-regulated, her vision so exalted, her ignorance so profound, her style alternately so preposterous and so perfect, that one despairs of ever reducing to the cold canons of criticism the inspired confusion of her works." [6]

But of ballads about the Duchess' visit to the Royal Society there is no trace today.

Wren and the Transfusion Experiments

Popular interest was particularly aroused by experiments some of the virtuosi had been undertaking by themselves and had later brought before the Society. These were on the transfusion of blood. Christopher Wren is credited with first proposing "the noble anatomical experiment of injecting liquors into the veins of animals" when he was in his late teens and early twenties at Wadham College with the other virtuosi. Wren had already been interested in anatomical matters; for as a lad in his early teens, after leaving school and before going down to Oxford in 1649, he had worked as a demonstrator for the well-known Dr. Charles Scarburgh in his public lectures at Surgeon's Hall in London. He had even made anatomical models out of pasteboard for the doctor to use in demonstrating the action of the muscles of the body. At Oxford he had worked with another famous doctor, Thomas Willis, on his classic dissections of the brain, drawing the plates of these dissections for Willis' book (1654).

Wren's many and varied interests included studies of the structure of fishes, the anatomy of the nerves, the human eye and the problems of vision. It was not surprising, therefore, that when only twenty-four years old, he was the one who suggested and first successfully demonstrated in 1656 the infusion of a liquid directly into a dog's veins. "By this Operation divers Creatures were immediately

[6] MacCarthy, *op. cit.*, 120.

purg'd, vomited, intoxicated, kill'd or reviv'd, according to the quality of the Liquor injected: Hence arose many new Experiments, and chiefly that of Transfusing Blood, which the Society has prosecuted in sundry instances, that will probably end in extraordinary Success." [7] How extraordinary, the wounded of World War II knew in the 1940's even if Sprat in 1667 could only guess.

Boyle and Wilkins were present at that first infusion, and perhaps others too. Using a syringe Wren injected tincture of opium through a quill into a vein which he had opened in a dog's hind leg. When the dog lapsed into a stupor, they all whipped and beat it into activity, thus keeping it alive. Rumors about the experiment led to the stealing of the dog. Nevertheless they kept at their tests with other dogs and other drugs, Wren characteristically and rapidly improving his techniques as he proceeded. Finally, in 1659 Wren successfully tried transfusion of blood through a quill directly from one animal into another. Interestingly enough, it has been pointed out that in the course of these experiments Wren had also by his use of the syringe introduced the idea of what we now know as the hypodermic needle, a device that had to wait for its full development until the nineteenth century.

In the midst of these transfusion experiments Wren returned to London to be Gresham professor of astronomy for some three years until in 1661 he was recalled to Oxford to be Savilian professor of astronomy there. During this time he continued work on his scientific ideas with the virtuosi, becoming not only an Original Fellow but also a member of the first Council of the Royal Society.

Wren himself, having proved his point that transfusion was possible and practical, had long since passed on to other problems and soon became deeply involved in the rebuilding of London after the Fire. Architectural matters were his major concern from that time on for the remainder of his long life; but he did not lose touch with the Fellows and their work. As president in 1680 for two

7 Sprat. p. 317

years he served them greatly, despite the pressure of his multifarious activities; after 1667, however, Wren was primarily the great architect, not the scientist that his earlier work had made him.

In May, 1665, Dr. Wilkins suggested to the Society that the experiment of injecting the blood of one dog into the vein of another might be tried; but they were busy then testing the oil of tobacco on small animals and birds. Next the Plague and the Fire intervened. At length, on March 28, 1667, the Society watched the bleeding of a sheep's blood into a spaniel's veins. Paris meantime had taken up the idea and was trying the transfusion of animal blood into man. When an insane man died while undergoing such a transfusion, the experiments were stopped. Dr. Wilkins during the summer read reports of these Paris experiments to the Royal Society. And on November 23rd, Dr. Richard Lower and Edmond King for the first time in England successfully performed a human transfusion for the Society. They introduced with no apparent ill-effect nine or ten ounces of blood from the artery of a sheep into a man variously described as a "harmless lunatic" and "an eccentric scholar." Thus they provided more curious ammunition for the wits and the critics to use in attacking the virtuosi. People speculated on what would happen to a man's nature if he received into his veins the blood of a lion or of a sheep.

Dr. Stubbs Against the Society

Popular interest in the new science stimulated in part by the kinds of experiments done, and in part by the lively controversies among the learned, developed still more under the attacks by the satirists and the ridicule of the poets and the dramatists. Among the learned opponents, the most prolific writer and the most virulent critic was Dr. Henry Stubbs. According to Anthony Wood, he was "a person of most admirable parts, of most prodigious memories (his enemies said he read indexes), the most noted Latinist and Grecian of his age . . . and a singular mathematician." His great talents we now know [8] were employed by Dr. Hamey, a fellow and a benefactor of the Royal College of Physicians, out of jealousy and fear of the Royal Society. This doctor was afraid of its growing power and especially of what it might do in the fields of medicine, anatomy and surgery, which he considered the rightful province of his own College. So he engaged Dr. Stubbs secretly to criticize the Society as vigorously and as violently at every point as he could. This just suited Dr. Stubbs, for he was "a man of as much acrimony as wit, with as knowing a head as he had an able hand and that wanted no ill nature to complete ye satirist in him."

What his contemporaries saw was that Stubbs "took a pet against the Royal Society," as Wood expressed it. He accused the virtuosi, either "very great impostors, or men of little reading," of attempting "to overthrow the universities and all others as idiots and ignoramus's," and claimed that "neither the ancients nor modern academicks were so foolish as they painted them out to be, nor the Royal Society so inquisitive as they would seem." That Protestants and Papists could converse together in friendly discourse as Sprat had said, he considered dangerous to religion. His concern, Stubbs asserted, was "the interest of the monarchy and religion in this land, the welfare of the Church or State, the happiness of this generation and of posterity." They on the other hand were seeking to undermine the universities, or at least to make them inconsiderable. They were seeking to destroy the established religion and to involve the nation in popery "and I know not what." So alarmed was he, as he claimed, that he was willing to hazard his life and fortune in pointing out these dangers; for he doubted whether "God would support us by His Providence, when they had debauched the Nation from all piety and morality, as well as civil wisdom."

8 See Harcourt Brown, *Scientific Organizations in Seventeenth Century France* (Baltimore, 1934) 256–257.

From Sprat's *History* and from other books, Stubbs found "undeniable arguments of the common danger, and the general and constant discourse as well as the deportment of the comical wits or virtuosi were such that no gloss or comment could create another representation of things." He pounced on the books of the young Joseph Glanvill, an ardent enthusiast of the new learning. He pointed out the laughter aroused among men of true learning and no strangers to mathematics, by the proposals some made of flying to the world in the moon, a design they thought superlatively ridiculous, though the contrivance of wings for mankind was then being projected, as he said, at Wadham College. He attacked the transfusion experiments, asking "what regulations shall we have for this operation, shall a man transfuse he knows not what, to correct he knows not what, God knows how?" To Robert Boyle, already one of the most distinguished and respected of the virtuosi, Stubbs wrote on June 4, 1670, "All men apprehend it now that their common interest is to oppose the Royal Society. I know not what physicians may, as the mode is, tell you to your face; but except it be such as Dr. Sydenham [9] and young Coxe, I believe that not one lives that doth not condemn your experimental philosophy." Stubbs' attacks were shrewd for his learning was great; but his language was intemperate and at times scurrilous, and his common sense and sobriety so lacking that he made himself and his learning cheap.

Joseph Glanvill was not easily silenced. He rose to the fray with further books and pamphlets pointing out that Stubbs had ignored Bacon's philosophy and had failed to note that the experimental philosophers were attacking not the ancients but their method. Glanvill pointed up his attack by asking, in reference to Stubbs' hair: "I said your head was red-*hot*. Why did you make yourself ridiculous at Oxford by plucking off your periwig and showing your

[9] Dr. Thomas Sydenham (1624–1689) called "the English Hippocrates," famous for his independence as well as for his work on fevers.

head to every freshman to demonstrate your charge of lying against me?"

The virtuosi, despite Glanvill's vigorous replies to these ill-tempered arguments, must have breathed a sigh of relief when they heard of Stubbs' accidental death in 1676. Not all could have been as serene and unconcerned under his whiplash of scorn and vituperation as Evelyn was when he wrote to Glanvill, on June 24, 1668, congratulating him upon his vindication of himself and of all useful learning against "the science (falsely so-called)" of his "snarling adversary." Evelyn went on: "I do not conceive why the Royal Society should any more concern themselves for the empty and malicious cavils of these delators, after what you have said; but let the moon-dogs bark on, till their throats are dry: the Society every day emerges, and her good genius will raise up one or another to judge and defend her; whilst there is nothing which does more confirm me in the nobleness of the design, than this spirit of contradiction which the devil (who hates all discoveries of those false and prestigious ways that have hitherto obtained) does incite to stir up men against it."

The Scoffers

But the moon-dogs or the devil were not stopped. Instead of the learned invective of a Stubbs or a South, the jokers, the satirists and the dramatists directed their pointed barbs at the Society in a manner hard to parry. Too often the laugh was on the virtuosi. The Fellows guarded themselves as best they could from the practical jokers. Of course they were eager to add to their repository specimens of every kind, even employing a collector in 1669 to travel through England and Scotland to assemble for them rarities of all sorts, and they welcomed gifts from outsiders as well as from their own members. But by 1668 the Society had to rule that gifts from outsiders, not Fellows, must first be shown to the president before they could be accepted, "for fear of lodging unknownly ballads and buffooneries in these scoffing times." So Oldenburg wrote to Boyle early in January that year.

The virtuosi in general and especially the Fellows knew well that they and their work were decidedly vulnerable to the ridicule of the scoffers. Had not the King himself laughed at their concern over the weight of the air? What could seem more futile than such experiments when the scientific study of the weather was in its infancy and the laws of barometric pressure were still being worked out? Observations with the telescope had been widely made and were generally known, but the enthusiasm of some of the amateurs and their excited imaginations had carried them into some surprising flights of fancy about possible voyages to the moon. Similarly the more recent work with the microscope seemed preposterous. Why was it important to see what the eye of a fly looked like? Such observations and inquiries, and many more besides, that the *Philosophical Transactions* were recording from month to month under Oldenburg's editorial hand were fine material for the satirists.

Sprat in particular had had the "wits and railleurs" of the age on his mind, hoping when he wrote his *History* to win them over to make common cause with the Royal Society, for "if they shall decry the promoting of Experiments, they will deprive themselves of the most fertil Subject of Fancy. And indeed it has been with respect to these terrible men that I have made this long digression [on the inexhaustible treasures of natural knowledge for the wits]. I acknowledge that we ought to have a great dread of their power. I confess I believe that New Philosophy need not (as Caesar) fear the pale of the melancholy as much as the humorous and the merry. For they perhaps by making it ridiculous, because it is new, and because they themselves are unwilling to take pains about it, may do it more injury than all the Arguments of our severe and frowning and dogmatical Adversaries." [10]

10 Sprat. p. 417.

What Sprat feared came to pass all too soon. Among the various writers attacking the Society's activities were Samuel Butler, Thomas Shadwell and Mrs. Aphra Behn, three of the most brilliant satirists to use this reservoir of experimental learning not, as Sprat had hoped, for their noble flights of fancy, but for the exercise of their wit and irony against the virtuosi and their activities. Butler to some extent differentiated between the enthusiast in pursuit of the new and strange, no matter how fantastic, and the true science-lover possessed of some common sense. The other two lumped them together as the common victims of their attacks.

Butler's poem "Elephant in the Moon," though written sometime in the 1660's or 70's, was not printed till 1759, together with a fragment "On the Royal Society" that was even more scathing. In the poem a group of virtuosi observe the moon one night through a long telescope. They discover that the moon's inhabitants are evidently at war and one claims to see an elephant striding across its surface. They fall into eager discussion about this, and a footman standing by decides to look for himself. He reports that he can see nothing because there is something in the tube near the eye-piece. A less credulous virtuoso looks and discovers a mouse caught in the tube. They all still debate violently the truth or falsity of their observations but finally decide to open the long tube. There they discover gnats, flies and other insects caught in it, and they realize that these were their great "armies battling" on the moon. Thus Butler ridiculed those who, misled by "tales stupendous and far fet," endeavored to explain "appearances, Not as they are but as they please, In vain strive Nature to suborn, And, for their pains, are paid with scorn." In the footman Butler typified the common sense of the ordinary individual who, without the learning of the virtuosi, uses his head instead of his imagination, and upsets the speculations of the learned men.

With equal scorn Butler wrote "On the Royal Society" about the Fellows:

"These were their learned speculations
And all their constant occupations:
To measure wind and weigh the air
And turn a Circle to a Square . . .
If Chymists from a Rose's ashes
Can raise the rose itself in Glasses . . .
To stew th'Elixir in a bath
Of Hope, Credulity, and Faith."

Though these verses were not printed till long after Butler's death in 1680, might they not have been passed around before then by word of mouth or from hand to hand? In all probability Butler was one of the "terrible men" whose mockery Sprat dreaded.

Far more deadly in its ridicule and less discriminating in its satire between the true virtuoso and the credulous one was Thomas Shadwell's play, "The Virtuoso," produced and also published in 1673. In this Shadwell created the famous character, Sir Nicholas Gimcrack, supposedly representative of the scholars absorbed in the new science without differentiating between the true scientist and the credulous enthusiast.

In the vocabulary of the Society's publications, Shadwell composed the dialogues. He drew the material for his scenes from the *Philosophical Transactions,* from Hooke's *Micrographia* and from Sprat's *History,* adding his own twist to what he used. Parodying the Society's study of insects and the tests they made on the supposed "eels in vinegar," he added stings to the eels' tails which gave vinegar its bite. He parodied the experiments on transfusion by recounting a transfusion of a spaniel into a bull-dog and of a sheep into a madman. He used what seemed the most fantastic of the virtuosi's activities, such as their studies of the possibility of flights by man, of the topography of the moon, of the density of the air, and by carrying them to extremes, he made scientific observation absurd. He made the virtuosi turn from the study of nature to a search for the philosopher's stone to serve mankind. Any attempt to differentiate between the true and the false virtuosi was lost in his play, and all were charged with "the artificial folly of those who are not coxcombs by nature, but with great art and industry make themselves so." Shadwell's twentieth century critic, Claude Lloyd, added: "The laugh was on the experimental science of the Royal Society."

The laugh was also on the experimenters themselves, for Sir Nicholas Gimcrack has lived on in literature. Certainly none of the virtuosi would care to be thought to have sat for this portrait of one of themselves. Various characters in Shadwell's play take their turn in describing him as "the finest speculative gentleman in the whole world . . . Not a creature so inanimate to which he does not give a tongue; he makes the whole world vocal; he makes flowers, nay weeds, speak eloquently and by a noble kind of Prosopopoeia instruct mankind." "He's an enemy to Wit, as all Virtuoso's are." He is "a sot, that has spent 2000 pounds in microscopes to find out the nature of eels in vinegar, mites in a cheese, and the blue of plums; which he has subtilly found to be living creatures." He has "broken his brains about the nature of maggots" . . . "has studied these twenty years to find out the several sorts of spiders, and never cares for understanding mankind."

His wife describes the well-known swimming lesson: "In his laboratory, a spacious room, where all his instruments and fine knick-knacks are . . . He has a frog in a bowl of water, tyed with a packthread by his loins; which packthread Sir Nicholas holds with his teeth, lying upon his belly on a table, and as the frog strikes, he strikes, and his swimming-master stands by to tell him when he does well or ill." Sir Nicholas himself remarks: "I swim most exquisitely on land." When asked if he intended to practise in the water, he replied: "Never, Sir, I hate the water . . . I never come upon the water, Sir." "Then there will be no use in swimming?" Sir Nicholas retorts: "I content myself with the speculative part of swimming, I care not for the Practick. I seldom bring anything to use; 'tis not my way. Knowledge is my ultimate end." One of his ques-

93

tioners satirically comments: "To study for use is base and mercenary, below the serene and quiet temper of a sedate philosopher." Another remarks: "I believe if the blood of an ass were transfus'd into a virtuoso, you would not know the emittent ass from the recipient philosopher."

Sir Nicholas dabbled in astronomy too. In talking about the moon, he knows it is like the earth for he can see "the larger sort of animals on it, as elephants and camels" and "publick buildings and ships very easily. I have seen several battles fought there. They have great guns, and have the use of gunpowder. At land they fight with elephants and castles. I have seen 'em."

In this play, called by another modern critic perhaps the most deadly of all the attacks upon the Society, Shadwell presented a picture of the virtuoso as "a crank, superstitious and gullible, and interested only in the eccentric or monstrous; a sham philosopher, vain and shallow, whose ostensible love of learning was at root but an idle curiosity, and whose learning itself was studiously divorced from practical reality." The play was immensely popular.

Hardly less deadly in its mockery was Mrs. Aphra Behn's farce, "The Emperor in the Moon," produced in London in 1687 and long a favorite. Again parodying the vocabulary of the virtuosi and their fantasies about people inhabiting the moon, the plot concerned the daughter and the niece of one of the virtuosi, a doctor, who has restricted the girls too closely. Scaramouche disguised as a man from the moon helps the two lovers similarly disguised to fool the doctor and get access to the girls. The plot was slight but there were dances and songs to add attractiveness to the ridicule of contemporary interest in lunar phenomena and their interpretations. Once more the virtuosi were the victims.

Cumulative Effects

Ridicule skillfully applied is indeed a dangerous weapon. The battle of the books could and did rage on for some decades to come, over the respective merits of the ancients and the moderns. But accusations of revolutionary activities against the state or against religion and the established church died down as Charles II passed through the twenty-five years of his reign, and as the age of rationalism drew near. Unquestionably the scoffers, the wits and the satirists, by their barbed thrusts, seriously weakened the development of the Royal Society after its first brilliant decade. The critical years for the Society were not those first ten years, but the next thirty. Neither Sprat's eloquent defense nor the power of royal patronage had sufficiently covered the vulnerable places. Surely the one new Fellow elected to membership in the Royal Society in 1690 reflected not only weakness within the Society as well as disturbed political conditions without, but also the cumulative effect of such brilliant satire as Shadwell's and such clever mockery as Mrs. Behn's. Who would have wanted to be considered a Sir Nicholas Gimcrack himself?

Some support for this contention may be found in William Wotton's *Reflections Upon Ancient and Modern Learning,* first published in 1694. He wrote: "Though the Royal Society has weathered the rude attacks of such as Stubbs who endeavour'd to have it thought that study of natural philosophy and mathematics was a ready method to introduce scepticism at least, if not atheism into the world: yet the sly insinuations of the Men of Wit that no great things ever were or are ever like to be perform'd by the men of Gresham and that every man whom they call a virtuoso must needs be a Sir Nicholas Gimcrack, together with the public ridiculing of all those who spend their time and fortunes in seeking after what some call useless natural rarities, who dissected animals, little as

95

well as great, who think no part of God's workmanship below their strictest examination and nicest search; have so far taken off the edge of those who have opulent fortunes, and a love of learning, that physiological studies begin to be contracted among physicians and mechanics. For nothing wounds so much as a jest; and when men do once become ridiculous, their labour will be slighted and they will find few imitators. How far this may deaden the industry of the philosophers of the next age is not easie to tell."

Would the Society survive the difficulties from within and the attacks from without? For years that question was unanswered, and for a time the critics seemed to be victorious. Though the virtuosi were fundamentally right in recognizing the unity of all knowledge and in searching out the answers to their questions by constant trial and experiment; yet the true scientists among them were less than a third of their number, and the amateurs among them were too often led astray into absurdities and fantastic speculations. The Society suffered in consequence. Nonetheless, the Society was accomplishing much useful work during these critical decades.

6

THE CRITICAL YEARS

ON JANUARY 11, 1671, the Journal-book of the Society recorded that, on the nomination of Dr. Seth Ward, then Bishop of Salisbury, Mr. Isaac Newton, professor of mathematics at Cambridge University, was elected a Fellow. In 1687, urged on by Halley, the astronomer, and sponsored by the Royal Society, Newton published his monumental *Principia*, enunciating the universal application of the law of gravitation. In 1703, when he had been in London since 1696, first as warden and then in 1699 as Master of the Mint, Newton was elected president of the Royal Society and was reelected annually until his death in 1727.

Some have said that with the publication of the *Principia* in 1687 the classical period of the Society's history came to an end and its development as a scientific society was assured. Lyons, however, points out that the last three decades of the seventeenth century were the difficult period in its life. Would it survive the death of some of its leading members, Wilkins in 1672, Moray in 1673,

Oldenburg in 1677? Would it solve its ever-present financial troubles? Would it again attract to itself enough scientifically-minded men to keep it in existence at all? Not even the prestige the Society received with Newton as its president for nearly a quarter of a century was an entirely adequate reenforcement. The membership question remained unsettled for a hundred years and more, and not till well on in the nineteenth century did the Society develop into the association of leading scientists that it is today. Yet, despite these unsettled questions, during the critical period of its existence at the close of the seventeenth century, the Society set in motion or sponsored a number of significant activities.

The Charters of the Society had set no limit to the number of its members or Fellows. After the original proposal in 1660 that they number fifty-five, this limit was soon removed and in 1663 one hundred and nineteen were listed as Original Fellows. Eleven more were elected later that year. By 1671, in addition to the Royal Patron and the Royal Fellows, there were 187 ordinary Fellows and foreign members. Yet, twenty years later there were only 116, less than the original charter group. In 1680 the meetings were so poorly attended that Evelyn wrote to Pepys in June asking for "one-half hour of your presence and assistance toward the most material concern of a Society which ought not to be dissolved for want of an redress . . . I do assure you we shall want one of your courage and address to encourage and carry on this affair. You know we do not usually fall on business till pretty late in expectation of a fuller company, and therefore if you decently could fall in amongst us by 6 or 7 it would, I am sure infinitely oblige . . . the whole Society." [1]

That year the Fellows sought to have as their president their best-known scientist, the Honorable Robert Boyle, in the hope perhaps that his great renown would re-establish the standing of their organization. Boyle had been liv-

[1] Cited in A. Bryant, *Samuel Pepys: The Years of Peril* (New York, 1935) 337.

ing in London since 1668 with his sister. Though he was in poor health, he refused the election not for that reason but because of his unwillingness to take the oaths required of the president.[2] The Council then turned to Sir Christopher Wren (he had been knighted in 1674) and under his active leadership instituted a number of administrative reforms concerning the payment of dues and fees. The next year twenty-three non-paying members including nine peers were struck off the rolls and twenty-five new members were elected, more than in any one year since 1667. Among these new members was William Penn, the founder of Pennsylvania.

The Period of Greatest Weakness

Sir Christopher was president for only two years as he had far too many other affairs to attend to as architect for St. Paul's and for many other public buildings being rebuilt after the Fire. Unfortunately, the Society's recovery under his presidency was only temporary, despite the efforts of his immediate successors. One of these, Samuel Pepys the diarist and Master of Trinity House, became Secretary to the Admiralty in his second and last year in the presidency. He had the honor as president of sanctioning for the Society the publication of Newton's masterpiece, the *Principia*.

The Royal Society in its *Record* has listed all its past presidents with brief annotations about their positions, distinctions and achievements. Pepys' successor in office, John, third and last Earl of Carbery, has one line giving the dates of his birth and death, and of the four years he was governor of Jamaica. Yet he was president for three years. One wonders why the Society elected this man who, as Lord Vaughan, was characterized by Pepys himself in 1667 as "one of the lewdest fellows of the age." He was a sworn enemy of Lord Clarendon who, Pepys claimed, "hath more friends in both Houses . . . by the reason

2 Cited in Lyons, 91.

that they do see what are the hands that pull him down." During his term as governor Lord Vaughan "made haste to grow as rich as his government would let him" and was charged with selling even his own servants. Lord Clarendon wrote of him: "A person of as ill a face as fame, his looks and manner both extreme bad." After these comments all the *Dictionary of National Biography* can say in his favor was that he had literary tastes and was one of Dryden's earliest patrons. It concludes that he was one of Charles II's most servile courtiers. But Charles was dead and his brother, the Duke of York, was ruling as James II. Perhaps his wealth and his succession to his father's earldom in 1686 were influential in securing the new Earl his election to the presidency.

After the Earl of Carbery's administration came that of the Earl of Pembroke, whose presidency of one year is notable in that he is said not to have attended a single meeting of the organization during that year,—1689-90. Perhaps he did not care to be too closely associated with a Stuart-supported group when his political star was rising under the favor of the new sovereigns. For in 1690, after the Bloodless Revolution, he became First Lord of the Admiralty under William and Mary, and under Anne, Lord-Lieutenant of Ireland and Lord High Admiral. He had, however, been a Fellow since 1685, for his antiquarian and mathematical interests did give him certain common interests with the science-lovers.

It is worth noting, also, that during these years that these two Earls were presidents, the publication of the *Philosophical Transactions* was suspended, not to be resumed till 1691. At that time Richard Waller as secretary took over the task of publication which Halley had held in 1686 and 1687. The failure to issue the *Transactions* is an important indication of the Society's weakness during this period, for the various issues were the chief indication of its activities not only for the membership as a whole but also for the learned world in Britain and abroad.

During the nearly thirty years of its organized existence

up to this time, the Society had had eight presidents. Its first, Lord Brouncker, was a distinguished mathematician as well as a loyal supporter of the Stuarts. Sir Christopher Wren, the third, was a remarkable scientist though the greater part of his long life was devoted to architecture. The other six are listed as statesmen and diplomats, or holders of high office under the Crown. Three could be considered virtuosi,—Hoskins, Wyche and Pepys. Two, Sir Joseph Williamson, Secretary of State and later a diplomat, and the Earl of Pembroke, even though a do-nothing president, at least had official distinction. But what can be said of the Earl of Carbery, except that he represents the lowest ebb in the long line of notable men who have been able to write P.R.S. after their names. It is not surprising that in 1689 the Society elected only four new members, in 1690 only one, and in 1691 just three. After that the tide turned as stronger leadership made itself felt.

The membership of a society with as weak leadership as that of the Royal Society in the late 'eighties and with the death or defection of some of its strongest members, could hardly fail to find the ridicule of the wits difficult to bear. The virtuosi could not have enjoyed being classed as Sir Nicholas Gimcracks, and might well have been reluctant to ally themselves publicly with a group so sharply criticized. One of his friends wrote to Dr. Sloane in 1687: "The Royal Society declines apace, not one correspondent in being." [3] The times were stormy, revolution impended, and until William and Mary were firmly established on the throne and freedom under law restored with their coming, the Society was indeed in a bad way. By the time of Newton's presidency thirteen years later, public affairs were steadied, membership in the Society had increased, and there were some 125 Fellows. Thereafter the membership grew steadily.

Whatever the factors affecting this membership situation—the public uncertainties, the critics, the lack of leadership—problems of money were almost hopelessly en-

3 Cited in C. E. Raven, *John Ray, Naturalist* (Cambridge, 1942), 243.

tangled with it. The weekly fee of a shilling a member from the very first had been disregarded by many of the Fellows, despite the efforts of the treasurer to collect it. At the annual meeting in 1663 the treasurer had to report that the members owed £158 and then, in 1670 that they owed £1475. The Society received no aid from the government and with one or two exceptions, gifts and bequests had not come in. Hampered thus financially, the Fellows in 1669 could not take up the request of the King that they measure a degree of latitude in a geodetic survey comparable to the one that the French scientists had just completed with the support of Louis XIV. They even were unable to pay in full at first the sums they had promised those who worked for them. Oldenburg, the hard-working secretary, protested repeatedly against being left "unassisted"; but for years he did not receive his full pay.

The Collections and the Library

William Ball, an astronomer who was the Society's first treasurer, on his retirement from that office in 1663 presented the Fellows with an ironbound chest with three separate locks (and one key for each of three officers) to hold their documents and their cash, a chest that the Society still treasures to this day (Plate 13). In it, Evelyn recorded, he had placed a gift of £100 towards their expenses. Another Fellow gave the same amount three years later which the Society used to buy a collection of rarities as the formal inauguration of its repository or museum. They already had had various oddities presented to them; now in 1668 they began a more systematic collection.

In those days there was no public museum or other place where specimens could be sent for preservation or for identification. The Society was therefore performing a useful and proper service in collecting, arranging and cataloguing specimens in natural science, however the wits might laugh. The collections grew rapidly. When Dr.

Nehemiah Grew published a catalogue and a description of the museum in 1681, the book was a folio of about 450 pages and listed by name 83 donors, including the East India and the Royal Africa Companies. A century later the Society gave these collections to the British Museum when it had to move to other quarters. There at the Museum the Society's collections were added to those already bequeathed in 1753 by Sir Hans Sloane, Newton's successor as president of the Society, to form the basis of the great Museum today.

Regardless of Sprat's disclaimer in his *Observations* of the Society's desire to collect a library, Evelyn proposed in January, 1667, to Henry Howard, later Duke of Norfolk, that he give the Society his ancestral collection of books and manuscripts. Howard was the Society's host at Arundel House for some years after the Fire of London, while the Gresham College building was being used by the City authorities. Evelyn, watching the books disappearing as visitors carried away volumes that appealed to them, suggested that the collection be turned over to the Society. Howard agreed and in 1678 more than 500 manuscripts and nearly 3000 printed books were transferred to the Society's rooms in the College. Some one hundred and fifty years later, in 1830, most of the manuscripts were turned over to the library of the British Museum, and the money given to the Society in return was spent for English and foreign scientific publications that were of more value to them than were the manuscripts on philosophical and theological subjects. As the Fellows down through the years have usually presented to the library copies of their publications, the Society today has a valuable library including many autographed first editions.

Expedients About Finances

Gifts of a library and specimens for a museum did not solve the Society's financial problems. Still the members did not pay their weekly shillings. In 1675 with the approval of the Attorney-General each newly elected Fellow thereafter was required to sign an agreement to pay each year in quarterly amounts fifty-two shillings, or £2.12s.od. But a year later the unpaid dues amounted to £2000. The Council of the Society tried various expedients from dunning letters to threats of lawsuits. In 1685 it listed forty-seven Fellows then in considerable arrears, informing them that their names would not be printed in the list of Fellows at the end of the year unless their debts were paid. Lawsuits were not actually undertaken, however, until 1728 when under the presidency of Sir Hans Sloane some were successfully carried through.

Disregarding their needs, the Council would on occasion release a Fellow from part or all of his dues when the circumstances seemed to justify it and the Fellow was important to the work of the Society.[4] And somehow or other through these critical years money did come in.

One particularly troublesome question was happily solved in this difficult period. While King Charles had granted the Royal Society no state subsidy, in 1669 he had turned over to the Fellows the Chelsea College lands. The gift proved burdensome indeed; the buildings were in bad repair, lawsuits threatened over various claims to the estate, and tenants were difficult to secure. The Fellows must have breathed a deep sigh of relief when the King expressed a desire in 1682 to have these lands returned to the Crown and in exchange promised them £1300, a promise unfortunately not kept.[5]

Nevertheless the financial difficulties continued. One or two small investments had been made by 1676 in the stock of the East India Company and of the Africa Company; but the sale of the East India Company stock was only narrowly averted in 1687 when one of the Fellows became

[4] Newton, for example. L. T. More, *Isaac Newton, a Biography* (New York, 1934) 154, 156, 252.

[5] Weld (I, 279) states that the Council voted to invest this sum in the East India Company. The present Librarian of the Royal Society says (in a letter January 6, 1948) that the grant was never paid.

personally responsible for the debt owed by the Society. When Dr. Hans Sloane became secretary in 1693, he tackled the financial problems with sufficient success to permit increased investment in the stock of the two companies after several years. Slowly the Fellows' payments were stabilized and made more regular, especially after the successful conclusion of several lawsuits. But throughout the first half-century of its existence, the lack of adequate financial support hampered the Society considerably and was a target for the critics, one that Dr. Henry Stubbs, for example, did not overlook.

The first considerable legacy the Society received was £400 from Dr. John Wilkins, Bishop of Chester, the man who throughout his life had been a devoted friend of science and of scientists, and a leader not only in the Royal Society but also in the Oxford Philosophical Society and in "the invisible college" preceding it. This legacy from the Bishop posed an interesting problem of investment for the young Society. It was nearly two years after his death in 1672 before the cash was turned over to the Society by his executors, and then only after prodding. The money was placed in the iron-bound chest while the Fellows debated what to do with it. The Mercers Company refused to accept it as a loan at interest. Proposals to purchase various houses were discussed and rejected. Finally in 1675 the money was invested in three fee-farm rents [6] in Sussex, bringing in £24 a year.

By 1703 the payment of these rents had been allowed to fall into arrears amounting to a debt of £450. An appeal in 1704 to the Chancery Court brought the decision nine years later that the estate holding the farms was obligated to pay both the annual rent and also the amount in arrears. For more than two hundred years these fee-farm rents continued to be paid. Characteristically enough, however, during the period of great laxity in the Society's ad-

6 Payments made in recognition of the occupant's obligation to the lord of the manor. A survival from the medieval system of land ownership, found similarly in the "ground rents" collected in Maryland.

ministration early in the nineteenth century, the annual payment was allowed to shrink to £19. 14s. od. without apparent cause. Finally, as Lyons reports, in 1937 the estate owning the farms sought release from these long continued annual payments and, after two years of negotiation, redeemed them by paying twenty-five years' rent, £570. Thus not until 1939 did Bishop Wilkins' legacy as invested in the fee-farm rents disappear as a separate item from the treasurer's report.

Support of Scientific Activities

While the Fellows for financial reasons could not undertake important scientific work like the geodetic survey the King had proposed, they could and did encourage and help scientific work in other ways. From the outset individual members in committees or in informal groups worked on questions which the Society wanted answered— a mode of procedure which the Society has used from that day to this. Boyle as a member of the "georgical" (agricultural) committee was one of those who agreed to have his gardener try planting the recently introduced potato as part of the Society's scheme to encourage its cultivation throughout England "as a way of preventing famine." This georgical committee planned to make lists of what plants were cultivated in England and several times at its meetings considered what winter greens (vegetables) were grown or growable. This same committee asked Sir William Petty, Dr. Wilkins and Robert Hooke to consider a suggestion by Hooke that London's water supply might be improved by increasing the flow of the Islington River.

The Committee of Correspondence in its turn planned a series of inquiries to be undertaken by travellers to the East Indies, and for seamen generally, but on the memorandum of the second meeting is the notation that "they never mett since Mr. Povey's feasting of them." The Society sent out inquiries to be made and requests for speci-

mens to be collected by persons going to far places,—to
Iceland, to South America, to India. Dr. Grew's *Catalogue*
of the Society's museum in consequence lists many objects
of all kinds from the Americas as well as from the other
continents. The Society as a whole and through its individual members was definitely trying to fulfil its purpose—
the promotion of natural knowledge.

Thus they encouraged each other to write various books
especially on the development of the crafts that had long
interested the virtuosi, as engraving, dyeing, the making
of glassware and the cultivation of orchard and other trees.
Beside their own *History* which they asked Sprat to write,
they gave their imprimatur of approval for publication to
Dr. Wilkins' *Essay toward a Real Character and a Philosophical Language* (1668), to Hooke's *Micrographia* (1665),
Evelyn's *Sylva, or a Discourse of Forest Trees* (1664), Malpighi's *Anatome Plantarum* (1675), Willughby's *Ornithol-
ogiae* supplemented by Ray (1676) and his *Historia
Piscium (History of Fishes)* (1686), several of Hooke's writings, Flamsteed's *Tide-Table for 1687* and Newton's *Principia* (1687),—to name only some of about thirty publications sanctioned, if not actually subsidized before 1700.
Through Oldenburg's *Philosophical Transactions* and
through Hooke's *Philosophical Collections* after Oldenburg's death, subscribers as well as members received abstracts or announcements of some of these books and were
informed about other scientific works published on the
continent as well as in England. The wide range and the
variety of the Society's interests and of the Fellows' activities are clearly evident in these different publications.

However, an indication of the serious uncertainties of
these years is registered by the absence of any book published in the Society's name after the *Principia* in 1687
until 1696. The lapse of three years in this same period in
the publication of the *Transactions* has already been
noted in connection with the presidencies of the two
Earls. Three editors had followed Hooke in quick succession when he stopped his *Philosophical Collections* (as

he called his issues of the *Transactions*) in 1682. After Halley ended his editorship (was he too absorbed that year in getting out the *Principia* for Newton?) there were no further issues until Waller undertook the task under the supervision of the Council. Since 1691 the *Transactions* have been issued every year.

Of course one of the great aids to scientists is just such information relating to their fields of interest as the *Transactions* could bring to them. The Royal Society was taking over the work of the earlier intelligencers, like Hartlib. Another great aid is the publication of scholarly works when commercial publishers see small chance of making any profit thereby. The Royal Society served scientists well by having important papers published in the *Philosophical Transactions* and by contributing to the cost of publication where a bookseller was unwilling to undertake the task without a subsidy. The Society gave five pounds and a copy of the book to the printer of Horrox's *Opera Posthuma*. It paid for the publication of Willughby's *History of Fishes* and it wanted to pay for the publication of the *Principia,* but it lacked the funds. Fortunately, Halley, a Fellow since 1678, though not a rich man was sufficiently enthusiastic over the importance of Newton's book to pay the costs himself for the Society. In that way, Newton's masterpiece was made available.

Services to English Style

At this point it might be well to note a less generally recognized but important service these early science-lovers of the Society rendered to the English language and to literary style. One of the virtuosi's complaints against the Aristotelianism of the university professors and against learned men generally, was that they used an over-elaborate style and a pedantic vocabulary that only the learned themselves could understand. The science-lovers on the other hand came to the conclusion that knowledge was for the general public, especially knowledge of the natural world. The facts of their investigations, the reports of their experiments should be as direct, straightforward and explicit as the investigations and experiments themselves. Sprat characterized it as a "naked" directness and simplicity of expression.[7]

Wilkins was a leader in developing this new style. Edmund Gosse, the English literary critic, wrote of him, "he was the first man in England to write commonly in the new kind of prose. His style deserves great praise. His sentences are short, pointed and exact . . . Justice has never yet been done him as a pioneer in English prose." One has only to dip into some of the writings of the earlier part of the seventeenth century and to compare them with Sprat's own *History* or with Wilkins' *Essay toward a real Character and a Philosophical Language* to note the difference.

In fact, the Royal Society in December 1664, and January 1665, included a study and reform of the English tongue as part of its early program, appointing Wilkins to meet with the committee of twenty-one members to improve the philosophy of the language. Evelyn also was asked to make suggestions and on June 20, 1665, replied with a long letter to the chairman, Sir Peter Wyche. His suggestions reflect his wisdom and his vision. They also in themselves are a commentary on the state of the English language in the seventeenth century. It has taken two centuries for most of his proposals to be put into effect. One of these, the omission of superfluous letters in words, like the second "o" in woomen and, for Americans, the "u" in honor has come about with the attrition of time; but simplified spelling as Evelyn advocated it, is still not generally adopted. However, English grammars have been compiled and rules laid down to make English a "learnable tongue" in line with Evelyn's ideas. English lexicons or dictionaries now exist giving first the "prime, certain and natural" meaning and then the symbolical. Technical

7 Sprat. 111–115.

terms have been collected from shops as well as from books. Determinations of weights, measures, coins, honors, obsolete or abrogated customs have been listed and explained. Exotic and unusual words have been expounded and idioms and proverbs collected. Foreign words for which there was no English equivalent have been made part of the language, such as "bizarre, concert, defer" and have become "good citizens." Examples of the best in ancient and modern prose and poetry have been collected as a guide for the improvement of taste and as an encouragement of the art of rhetoric.

All these Evelyn recommended; but their development has come about not primarily through the efforts of the Royal Society's committee but as later ages realized and met the need. The Society's committee seems not to have been active, and the improvement of the English tongue came about as a by-product of the Society's activities rather than as a main end to be achieved. The Royal Society after that first effort did not thereafter attempt to parallel the work of the *Académie Française* in standardizing the language.

Dr. Wilkins' labors on his *Essay* and the help of his friends had other values besides that of finding the exact word to express an idea in naked simplicity. His search for some form of a universal written language that could be read by the people of any nationality as easily as the notations in a piece of music or the symbols in mathematics are read, led him to try to classify all knowledge and to reduce it to its bare essentials, in order to express those essentials by written symbols or signs. A written expression for the term dog, for instance, could have an added symbol to indicate a certain kind of dog, as a hound. The symbols he used in the writing or "character" he described in his *Essay* naturally required a kind of dictionary to accompany them that would help to place the idea to be expressed in its proper classification among the symbols.

In working out these classifications Wilkins had the

help of some of his younger friends, notably that of Francis Willughby and John Ray, the two foremost naturalists of their time. One of their biographers claims that this endeavor under Wilkins' guidance to classify knowledge of the natural world gave them an impetus toward their own later scientific work on the classification of plants and of fishes.[8] Wilkins' classifications were also followed in the arrangement of the Society's museum specimens, and through Grew's printed *Catalogue* continued to be of influence on classification long after Wilkins had died. His *Essay* had attempted the impossible under the limitations of that time and is now itself merely a curiosity in scientific history. But the Royal Society had encouraged him to write it and had sponsored its publication. Thus indirectly through such by-products, so to speak, the Society served the English tongue better than the Fellows had with the large committee they had set up for that purpose, a committee that never reported.

The Society and the Royal Observatory

During these critical years at the end of the seventeenth century the Society rendered a direct and notable service to science in connection with the Royal Observatory. This institution was established in 1675 at Greenwich by Charles II on a site suggested by Sir Christopher Wren and erected according to his plans. Dr. John Flamsteed was the first "Astronomical Observator" by royal appointment.

Dr. Flamsteed was another of these science-lovers who earned their living in some other field, yet seemed to give most of their time, thought and money to their scientific pursuits. His plan was to take charge of a parish and at the same time to continue with his astronomical studies. He had long since discovered how inaccurate were the current astronomical tables and how great was the need for the more precise foretelling of celestial phenomena.

8 G. S. Boulger, "John Ray" *Dict. of Nat. Biog.*

He had prepared such a revised almanac for 1670 and had sent it up to the Royal Society. In time he himself came up to London to meet his various correspondents among the virtuosi. They welcomed him and gave him additional instruments as well as other help. These men also talked about Flamsteed's work with the King and his brother, the Duke of York.

By 1674 the Royal Society was considering setting up its own observatory, possibly under the direction of Flamsteed, when a Frenchman appealed to the King for his help; he had "solved the problem of finding the longitude at sea." Until the chronometer was invented in the eighteenth century, finding a ship's longitude at sea was a very difficult problem. Local time was easily ascertained, but standard time at the prime meridian was most difficult to learn. Yet the difference of the two times measures the longitude of the observer east or west of the prime meridian. The Frenchman's scheme was to use the shifts of the moon's positions among the fixed stars as a basis for calculation.

Charles referred the matter to a committee that included with some others, nine Fellows, among whom were Wren, Hooke, and Moray. Flamsteed, then in London, came to one of the meetings of this committee and pointed out the inaccuracies in the existing star-catalogues. Charles was "startled at the assertion of the fixed stars' places being false in the catalogue" and said he "must have them anew observed, examined, and corrected, for the use of his seamen." Forthwith he appointed Flamsteed the first Astronomer Royal and ordered the construction of an observatory not to cost more than £500.

The next year, 1676, the building was completed and Flamsteed installed; but all the equipment consisted of a sextant and two clocks which were the gift of one of the mathematicians in the Royal Society. The King characteristically had made no provision for equipment nor for expenses other than Flamsteed's salary. The Fellows came to Flamsteed's aid by lending him their own astronomi-

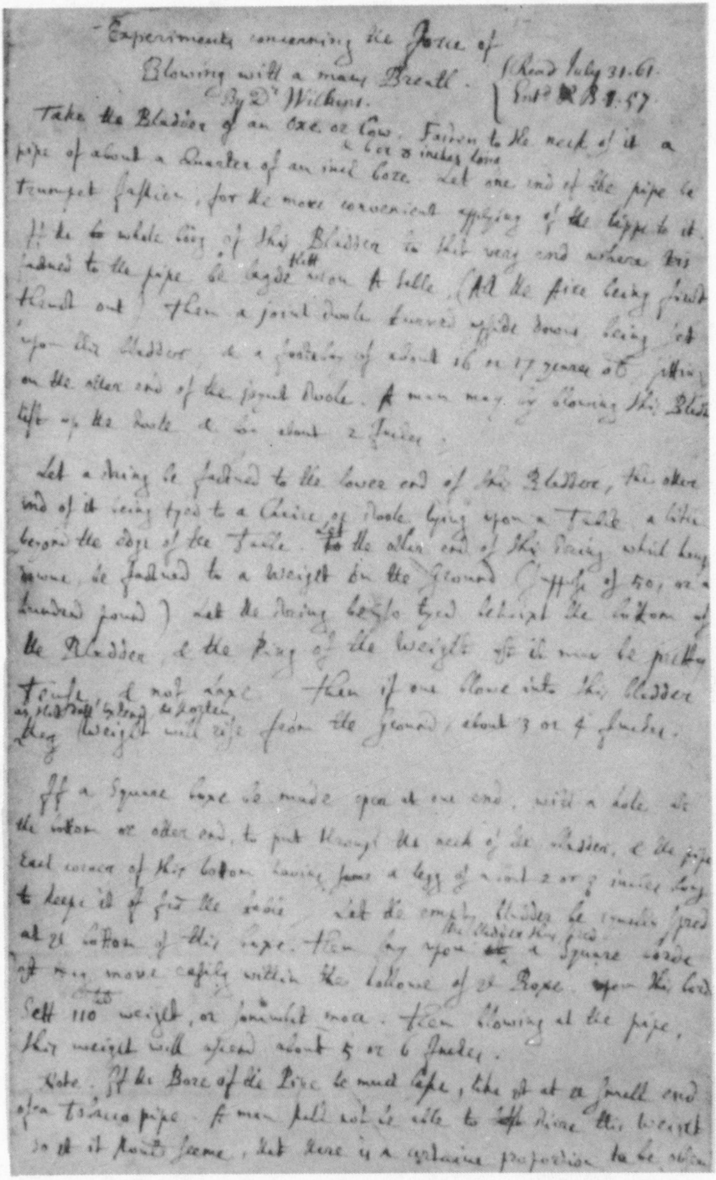

Experiments concerning the Force of Blowing with a mans Breath. By Dr Wilkins.

Read July 31. 61. Entd R.B. 1. 57

Take the Bladder of an Oxe or Cow. Fasten to the neck of it a pipe of about a Quarter of an inch bore & 6 or 8 inches long. Let one end of the pipe be trumpet fashion, for the more convenient applying of the lipps to it. If the whole body of this Bladder in this way and where tis fastned to the pipe be layde flatt upon a table (All the aire being first thrust out) then a joint stoole turned upside downe being set upon this bladder, & a youth of about 16 or 17 yeares old sitting on the other end of the joint stoole. A man may by blowing this Bladder lift up the stoole & him about 2 Inches.

Let a string be fastned to the lower end of this Bladder, the other end of it being tyed to a Peice of Stoole lying upon a Table a little beyond the edge of the Table. Let the other end of this String which hangs downe be fastned to a weight on the ground (of 50 or a hundred pound) Let the string be so tyed betwixt the bottom of the Bladder & the Ring of the weight that it may be pretty tense, & not laxe. Then if one blowe into this bladder as stiff & strong as he is able, the weight will rise from the ground about 3 or 4 Inches.

If a Square boxe be made open at one end, with a hole in the bottom or other end, to put through the neck of the bladder, & the pipe. Each corner of this bottom having some a legg of about 2 or 3 inches long to keepe it of from the table. Let the empty bladder be smoothly spred at the bottom of this boxe. then lay upon the bladder thus spred a Square borde that may move easily within the hollowe of the Boxe. upon this bord sett 110 120 weight, or somewhat more. Then blowing at the pipe, this weight will ascend about 5 or 6 Inches.

Note. If the Bore of the Pipe be much less, like that at the small end of a tobacco pipe. A man will not be able to raise this weight so well as it would seeme, but there is a certaine proportion to be obse

PLATE 10. Experiments concerning the Force of Blowing with a Man's Breath reported by Dr. Wilkins, July 31, 1661

(From the original manuscript in the Library of the Royal Society, by courtesy of the Royal Society)

PLATE 11. Frontispiece of Sprat's *History of the Royal Society* with the inscription by Dr. Wilkins

(From *The Record of the Royal Society*, London, 1940, by courtesy of the Royal Society)

cal instruments for two years until they reclaimed them again for their own use. They also elected him a Fellow in 1677. With what instruments he had, Flamsteed went to work, drawing upon his own funds for further equipment. The result of his labors was the preparation of a star-catalogue of nearly 3000 stars (the best up to then had had only 1000) with an accuracy that reduced prevailing errors from several minutes to only a few seconds.

Meantime the Royal Society was in the closest touch with Flamsteed. Newton, Halley and the others needed his accurate observations for their own work and they wanted publication of his findings as soon as possible. Flamsteed wanted to wait until he had completed them. The result was a bitter quarrel in the astronomer's later years over an imperfect and unauthorized publication of some of his observations in 1712, secured by Newton and Halley without his consent. Some years later Flamsteed was able to recover the unsold copies and, having done so, began to arrange for publication in full at his own expense. He could not do this before, both because he wanted to complete his work and because he had to finance the publication from his own resources. Because he had no help from the government aside from his small salary, he had had to take private pupils to supplement his income. Altogether he spent about £2000 of his own funds on the work of the observatory. Before he could complete publication he died in 1719, and his friends and helpers had to finish the task for him. The three volumes appeared in 1725.

Queen Anne in 1710 had appointed Newton, then President of the Royal Society and such other Fellows as the President thought fit, to be Visitors of the Observatory. Years later to the five Visitors from the Royal Society were added five from the Royal Astronomical Society together with the professors of astronomy from Oxford and Cambridge. Later still an officer from the Navy was appointed and the professors no longer used. That Board of Visitors has continued ever since.

The Royal Observatory in Wren's building, with others erected later, has been in operation ever since. But astronomical work at Greenwich has become too hampered in recent years by the spread of city life with the vibrations resulting from increasingly heavy traffic and with the glare from night lights, together with the bomb damage of the war years. So in 1946 the removal of much of the equipment and of the work to a quiet place in Sussex was begun. But "Greenwich time" will continue to standardize the world's clocks.

This close relationship between the Royal Society and the Royal Observatory is not only the oldest but also the first of a long series of consultations about scientific institutions and scientific matters for which the government has turned with increasing frequency to the Fellows of the Royal Society for advice and help, from that day to this. In later chapters there will be more proof of this.

The End of a Period

Long before 1700 the most vivid and colorful years of the Society's history were over, but now also the critical ones were ending too. An important new problem still had to be faced, that of housing, for the Gresham College building after more than a century's hard use was in a sad state. However, thanks to Dr. Sloane's efforts as secretary, the accounts of the Society were in better shape, and the size of the membership had increased a little, giving signs of further growth. The *Philosophical Transactions*, under the Council's oversight after 1690, were appearing regularly. A long list of notable books had been either published or sponsored by the Society. The library and the museum were well established and were growing steadily. There were foreign members in Europe and other Fellows in the colonies, and their foreign correspondence was heavy. The Society was already renowned in learned circles at home and abroad, in spite of the critics and the wits.

114

It continued, of course, to be a society of "gentlemen," not all of them even amateurs of science, and certainly less than a third true scientists; but scientists have not been numerous anywhere until relatively recently. The fundamental problem of the proper qualifications for membership would not be solved until well on into the nineteenth century. However, it was largely because of these "gentlemen" that the new science secured a hearing and received much needed encouragement. These men were its patrons and protectors. They provided funds, equipment and a critical, keenly interested hearing for the workers they themselves recognized as making genuine scientific progress. Naturally they fumbled and groped with what seems to us, perhaps, amazing naïveté; but without the backing of these amateurs, the Royal Society would hardly have survived, nor possibly would science itself have progressed as rapidly as it has in the past two centuries.

As the Society entered upon the eighteenth century, it could face its immediate future hopefully. With Newton's election to the presidency in 1703, the critical years of the organization had come to a close.

7

STABILITY

OBVIOUSLY the Royal Society was not developing independently of the life around it, however remote from reality its researches seemed to its critics. As time passed the Society must inevitably either shrivel and die or else draw strength from the environment to which it was making its own contribution. As yet, however, the viability of the Society was still uncertain. Criticisms and quarrels continued; but Newton's long presidency gave it both prestige and permanence. Under Sloane, Newton's co-worker in the Society and his successor, the Society continued to gain in numbers and financial strength; but Sloane was more a patron of science than a scientist. So also was Sir Joseph Banks whose presidency covered the close of the eighteenth and the beginning of the nineteenth centuries. In many respects the problems which the Society faced under Newton at the opening of the century were similar to those which confronted it under Banks at the close. During the eighteenth century the leadership of the Society in scientific work wavered and slackened as the Society became more and more like a gentleman's social club. Fundamental reorganization and development had to await the reforms of the nineteenth century.

All three—Newton, Sloane and Banks—as presidents were strong administrators but less scientists than patrons of science. Even Newton during his old age, after his *Opticks* was published in 1704, was more concerned with history, religion and the problems of chronology presented in the Old Testament than he was with sustained creative scientific work.[1] His great work had been done both in science and in national service before he was elected president. His position as Master of the Mint from 1699 until his death involved fairly routine matters, though it was not the sinecure that it has been called. Furthermore, Hooke's death early in 1703 had removed from the Society one of Newton's most jealous and quarrelsome critics, one whom Newton had avoided meeting whenever possible. Now he could give time and attention to the affairs of the Society in which he had been a Fellow for more than thirty years. His presidency gave the Society security because of his personal prestige and scientific eminence.

After Sloane resigned in 1741, however, the influence of the scientists among the officers and the Council diminished and weaknesses developed dangerously. The Fellows who were historians and antiquarians, not scientists at all, increased in number and importance. This chapter and the next will consider the affairs of the Society in the administrations of Newton and Sloane. Then in the following chapters will be presented some of the major activities of the Fellows in the same century as they helped to place Sir Joseph Banks in the presidency and to keep him there until his death. Unavoidably there will be a certain amount of overlapping in such a division; for growth is not necessarily continuous and all of a piece, even though its recorder may have to present it that way.

1 L. T. More. *Isaac Newton, a Biography* (New York, 1934) pp. 514, 519.

Conditions in England

First, a glance at conditions in England during the early eighteenth century may serve as an aid to a better comprehension of the Society's varied interests and concerns. Newton came to the presidency early in the reign of Queen Anne, last of the Stuart rulers. He died at the close of the reign of George I, first of the Hanoverian line on the British throne. That the change over to the Georges was not made without a struggle, is proved by the uprising of '15 and confirmed by that of '45. As a result England was yet more closely involved in the complexities of continental relationships and problems. Within England under the German-speaking King, management of the government devolved upon the leaders in the Whig party that had supported his accession to the throne. Thus Robert Walpole became the first prime minister. But while Parliament was itself supreme, having determined who should reign in England and who should not, it was nevertheless under the control of the landlords and the rich. Relatively few people had the right of suffrage, the vote was open, and the voting period long. "Every man has his price" and Walpole and his party acted accordingly.

The effects of the commercial revolution of the preceding centuries,—the development of business and of great fortunes derived from trade and commerce, the growth of stock companies and of banking—had already begun the marked shift from power based on vast landed estates to power based on large amounts of capital, from country life to city life, from production for little more than subsistence to production for profit made as rapidly as possible. England even under the later Stuarts, like the Low Countries and Prussia, had benefited from the coming of the French Huguenots, fleeing from the renewal of persecution after Louis XIV had revoked the Edict of Nantes in 1685. They were an industrious people, with skilled workers in many trades, especially weaving. Some were men of wealth and learning, while all were steadfast. Some of these exiles remained in England. Others, after a few years, sailed across the Atlantic to add their skills and their culture to the colonies, an addition registered not merely in city names, like New Rochelle, and on the tombstones in the cemeteries, but in the evident French ancestry of some of their American descendants today. Theirs was a peculiarly dominant strain.

The rapid growth in wealth by the few aroused the cupidities of the many. Gambling in the shares of companies formed to do business of all sorts and even of none, resulted in a mad wave of speculation that swept over England, France and the Low Countries after the great European war, known as the "Spanish Succession," had come to an end. For a new king was on the throne in France as well as in England, and peace seemed permanent once more. The inevitable financial crash came with the bursting of the South Sea Bubble and of several similar schemes. But already the great movements of this century—agricultural, industrial, and religious—were under way. Steam engines were being studied and tried, improvements in weaving had begun, and experiments with turnips for winter fodder for cattle were making possible the improvement of the herds. The wealthy were not now content to remain on their estates the greater part of the year, but began to build beautiful eighteenth century town houses in London and in other cities, and to develop squares and places filling in the areas between the mile-square City of London and the outlying districts such as Westminster and Kensington.

Though there was great wealth, there was still greater poverty. Beggars roamed the streets by day, highwaymen and thieves made them dangerous at night. To man its ships, the government used press-gangs who dragged the able-bodied from the streets to the docks. Great fortunes were being made in shipping captive Negroes from their African homelands, to be sold as slaves in the markets of the New World. It was a coarse and violent age, as anyone who has seen Hogarth's caricatures can well imagine. Even the Church of England was not, in general, much better. Many of its clergy were as corrupt, as ignorant, and as in need of reform as the society of which they were a part. Their unsatisfied parishioners were to provide a rich soil for the reforms of the Methodist movement which spread throughout England and into the colonies, under the leadership of the Wesleys and of Whitefield.

During the early years of this century there seems at first glance little connection between the activities of the Royal Society and public life. The Society had been a favorite project of Charles II. His brother, James II, had been elected a Fellow when he was still Duke of York. Neither William nor Mary had signed the Charter-book of the Society during their reign, perhaps naturally enough since they were on the throne of England by the will of Parliament and not by reason of Mary's Stuart lineage. Would they be likely to look with favor on a Society many of whose members had been at the courts of Charles and James? No wonder the prestige of the Society was clouded in those years just before Newton came to the presidency in 1703.

Newton as President

Within a year after his election, Newton succeeded in persuading Prince George of Denmark, Queen Anne's consort, to accept membership in the Society. Thus once again after a long lapse, close connections were reestablished with the court. Queen Anne, always appreciative of courtesies paid to her husband, indicated her royal favor by bestowing knighthood upon Newton the day she spent visiting Cambridge University in 1705. More, Newton's recent biographer, calls this an unprecedented expression of the unique position Newton occupied in his world, for no scientist before, except Wren, had been so honored and Wren, he claimed, had been knighted more for his public work than for his scientific eminence. Yet Wren was knighted in 1673 by Charles II very early in his architectural career and after his scientific achievements had been many and renowned. Was not his knighthood at that time for scientific eminence as well? It is true also that Sir William Petty was knighted (in 1662); but this seems to have been based more on his services to the government in Ireland and in the field of economics than in science. Be that as it may, Sir Isaac Newton was now foremost among scientists by a royal recognition that helped him politically, for he was a moderate Whig, as well as the Royal Society of which he was the president.

Prince George expressed his appreciation of his election to the fellowship by agreeing to defray the cost of publishing Flamsteed's catalogue of the stars. Delays ensued, the Prince died, and the committee in charge, dominated by Newton, turned to Halley to bring out the edition. These were the years of the long and bitter controversy between Newton and Flamsteed to which reference has already been made.

One gathers the impression from this affair that Newton was a rather high-handed, determined old gentleman, an impression strengthened by the way he carried through the removal of the Society from Gresham College to new quarters in Crane Court.

After well over a century of hard use, Sir Thomas Gresham's old home had become thoroughly dilapidated, costing the Mercers Company heavily for repairs at a time when the Company itself was financially embarrassed. Would it not be wiser to tear down the old buildings, sell some of the land, and rebuild the College on a more convenient plan? In this way the Society could also continue to share the buildings with the College and both could profit from the library, the collections and the opportunities provided by such an educational and scientific center in the City. Parliament had to approve, as this involved trust funds, but because of Hooke's violent opposition, the bill was thrown out in 1701. After Hooke's death, the bill was reintroduced, incorporating suggestions made by Wren for the needs of the Society, together with a clause requiring completion of the rebuilding within five years, subject to a heavy penalty. This too failed to pass. As there seemed no further prospect of any immediate rebuilding, the Council of the Society started, just before Newton's presidency, to consider the housing problem confronting them.

Wren's specifications in 1703 for adequate housing of the Society[2] are interesting. The building should be so situated as to provide easy access "for the coaches of the members (some of which are of very great quality)" and should have three storeys and a "good cellar underground so high above it as to have good lights for the use of an elaboratory [sic] and housekeeper." On the main floor would be a fair room with a large closet, next above it the repository and on the top floor the library, with the roof covered with lead for observing the heavens. A good staircase was to run from bottom to top and there must be plenty of space in back of the building to give light to the back rooms. Ground with a forty foot frontage and a depth of sixty feet would be adequate. Wren's plan still remains in the archives of the Society, with the various dimensions carefully worked out.

The Society had neither the land nor the money available for building. Meanwhile the Mercers Company in 1705 notified the Society that they had resolved not to grant it any room at all in the College. Accordingly the Council considered many avenues, unavailingly, until finally in September, 1710, Newton as president informed the Fellows of a house in Crane Court about to be sold that might be suitable as it was "in the middle of town and out of noise." This information was laid before a special session called just before the Council meeting.

An anonymous pamphlet of the period, Weld reports, described the surprise and dismay of the Fellows when

2 Cited in Lyons, 132.

Newton told them of the proposed move and asked for any objections to it. Apparently the Council had not kept the Fellows, as a whole, in touch with its difficulties nor with the decision of the Mercers Company not to grant them room any longer. The Fellows protested that they were comfortable and satisfied where they were and that the Society had met in the College from the very first. Why was it necessary to move now? Newton is quoted as replying, "That he had good reasons for their removing, which he did not think proper to be given there." He was supported by Dr. Hans Sloane, then the secretary, whose management both of the Society's affairs and of its president, the anonymous writer considered despotic. The Fellows were not satisfied and asked for a delay until the annual meeting the end of November, or at least until another special meeting of the Fellows could be called. Newton refused to consider this, nor would he allow an expression of opinion on the matter by the taking of a vote. Whereat the meeting broke up, leaving Newton, Sloane and two or three others to handle affairs at the Council.

Crane Court

The Council finally approved the purchase of the Crane Court property with the little house adjoining it, borrowing the money for the purpose. The cost of the necessary alterations and repairs also had to be met. For these, a number of gifts were made by the Fellows, including £190 [3] from Newton himself.

On November 8th, 1710, the Society met in its own house for the first time. Soon thereafter the library and the collections were installed and the close connection with Gresham College came to an end. To the prestige of Sir Isaac Newton's presidency was now added the sta-

---

[3] The *Record,* printing the Council's minutes (p. 141) gives this amount. More (p. 504) says Newton gave £190; Lyons (p. 142) says £120; Craig (p. 77) says £110.

bility of a permanent home, one which the Society was to occupy for seventy years, even longer than it had been at Gresham College. The Society's gain was the College's loss. For many years the Society's presence and activity in the Gresham College buildings had been at the service of the professors as well. The professors who were Fellows had also by courtesy been excused from the regular fees. With the removal of the Society to Crane Court all that was changed, and the College's historian lamented the Society's departure.

Yet Gresham College went on and still exists today. The original College buildings continued in use, in spite of their dilapidated condition, until 1768 when by Act of Parliament the trustees surrendered them to the government in return for a room in the Royal Exchange and £500 a year. After a couple of other shifts of location, the trustees in 1843 erected a building for the College in Gresham Street. In 1913 this too was replaced by the present tall office building. This building still stands, despite the bombing of the City of London, to startle the sightseer by the College name on a modern office building—an unexpected reminder of an honorable, century-long record in an eventful period in the history of ideas. Sir Thomas Gresham's desire to make available to the citizens of London the learning of the day, was both useful and fruitful for many years. Nearly three hundred and fifty years since his death and the opening of his College, the name and the trust continue, though his original plan, unique at its outset, has long since been modified. Since 1876, for example, all lectures have been given in English. In recent years four lectures in each of the seven subjects continue to be given each term with free admission; and some, it is said, are well attended.

What was the Crane Court house like? Its description by the anonymous writer, quoted by Weld, forms an interesting comparison with Wren's proposals:

"The approach to it, I confess, is very fair and handsome through a long court: but then they have no other property in this than in the street before it; and in a heavy rain a man can hardly escape being thoroughly wet before he can pass through it. The front of the house, towards the garden is about 42 ft. long; but that towards Crane Court not above 30 foot. Upon the ground-floor there is a little hall, and a direct passage from the stairs into the garden about 4 or 5 foot wide; and on each side of it, a little room about 15 ft. long and 16 ft. broad. The stairs are easie which carry you to the next floor. Here there is a room fronting the Court, directly over the hall, and of the same bigness. And towards the garden is the Meeting-room, which is 25½ foot long and 16 foot broad. At the end of this room there is another (also fronting the garden) 12½ foot long and 16 foot broad. The three rooms upon the next floor are of the same bigness with those I have last described. These are all that are as yet provided for the reception of the Society; except you will add the garrets, a platform of lead over them, and the usual cellars &c. below, of which they have more and better at Gresham College. The garden is but 42 foot long, and 27 broad, and the coach-house and stables are 40 foot long, and 20 foot broad."

Here under its own roof, the Society was to stay till 1780 when it moved into the rooms offered it by the government at Somerset House. Here visitors to London came to see the most remarkable collections of rarities up to that time available to the curious. Here came Voltaire, Benjamin Franklin, Maupertuis, Buffon, Réaumur, Montesquieu, lords (but not ladies), high churchmen, ambassadors, writers, divines, doctors, and guests from far and near. Many, like those named, were proud to accept election to membership in the Society; others were interested in the people of "very great quality" they saw there as well as in the discussions, and still others, as will be seen, having come, were bitter because they had *not* been elected to membership in what was still more a club of notables than a scientific association.

Here Newton came regularly to preside over the meetings to the wonder and awe of visitors, even though one of these visitors was to record that the famous old man had opened the meeting, then slept peacefully in his chair until the end.[4] As he grew old and feeble an effort was made to relieve him of some of the cares of office and Sir Hans Sloane, in 1720, was made a vice-president. But till his death in 1727 Newton continued in the presidency, and is to this day considered the most distinguished of all who have held that office.

His death and that of Sir Christopher Wren, not long before, brought to a close the period in which a few men still knew at first hand about the Society's early days. Pepys had died long before, in 1686, followed by Boyle in 1691. Hooke had lived on until 1703, growing ever more irascible, while Evelyn had lived till 1706 and Sprat till 1713. Wren, who had continued active until his death early in 1723, and Newton were the exceptionally long-lived members.

Contemporary Interest in the Society

The passing of these leaders notable in the early life of the Society, combined with the discussions about the removal from Gresham College, must surely have aroused considerable interest in the Society's origins. Why else would there have been a new edition of Sprat's *History* in 1702 even though Dean Jonathan Swift called it "the best book in the English language"? Hans Sloane, so he told Newton's nephew-in-law, had often pressed others to continue it but in vain. "Sprat's first sketch which was intended as a sample and to encourage others to continue it was written with such perfection that no one durst continue." Among other re-issues, in 1705 there appeared a collected edition in one volume of Wilkins' mathematical and "philosophical" works, and also a *Miscellanea Curiosa* reprinting papers from the Society in two volumes, with a third volume following some years later. Then, too, a collected edition of Boyle's works was published early in the seventeen-twenties.

Definite proof of contemporary interest in the Society

[4] Cited by More, *op. cit.* 457.

and its activities comes from essays in the *Spectator* and the *Tatler,* even though Addison and Steele wrote in ridicule and disparagement. Would they have written at all, had not the Society's affairs been subjects of general discussion at the time? In October of 1710, just after the decision in favor of the Crane Court house had been pushed through, Steele commenting in the *Tatler* (No. 236) on the frequent elections in "our" Royal Society remarked: "They seem to be in a confederacy against men of polite genius, noble thought and diffusive learning; and choose into their assemblies such as have no pretense to wisdom, but want of wit; or to natural knowledge but ignorance of everything else. I have made observations in this matter so long that when I meet a young fellow that is a humble admirer of science, but more dull than the rest of the company, I conclude him to be a F.R.S."

A year later in the *Spectator* (No. 262) Addison wrote about the improvement of natural knowledge: "Among these advantages . . . it is not the least that it draws men's minds off from the bitterness of party and furnishes them with subjects of discourse that may be treated without warmth or passion. This is said to have been the first design of those gentlemen who set on foot the Royal Society; and had then a very good effect as it turned many of the greatest geniuses of that age to the disquisitions of natural knowledge, who, if they had engaged in politics with the same parts and applications, might have set their country in a flame. The air-pump, the barometer, the quadrant, and like inventions were thrown out to those busy spirits, as tubs and barrels are to a whale, that he might let the ship sail on without disturbance, while he diverts himself with those innocent amusements."

Like Shadwell, Butler and the other writers in the last decades of the seventeenth century, both essayists again and again poked fun at the Fellows and ridiculed their activities. Steele, making use of a Fellow's advocacy of cold baths, recounted the autobiography of a month old baby who had been neglected and not fed, and was pining away. Then came this F.R.S. who protested the baby was utterly lost for want of that method and promptly soused him head and ears into a pail of water, "where I had the good fortune to be drowned." (*Tatler*, No. 15.)

Addison, commenting on "one of these whimsical philosophers" who set greater value on collections of spiders than on a flock of sheep and sold a coat to purchase a tarantula, went on, "I would not have a scholar unacquainted with these secrets and curiosities of nature (as the generation of a mite) but certainly the mind of man, that is capable of so much higher contemplations, should not be altogether fixed upon such mean and disproportionate objects. Observations of this kind are apt to alienate us too much from the knowledge of the world, and to make us serious upon trifles, by which they expose philosophy to the ridicule of the witty, and the contempt of the ignorant . . . Studies of this nature should be diversions, relaxations and amusements; not the care, business and concern of life . . . I have been shown a beetle valued at 20 crowns, and a toad at a hundred . . . Whatever looks trivial or obscene in the common notions of the world, looks grave and philosophical in the eye of a virtuoso."

Sir Nicholas Gimcrack Again

Whereupon Addison picked up Shadwell's famous character, Sir Nicholas Gimcrack, and proceeded to write his will. To his wife Sir Nicholas according to Addison left one box of butterflies, one drawer of shells, a female skeleton and a dried cockatrice. To his daughter Elizabeth, he left his receipt for preserving dead caterpillars, his preparation of winter May-dew and his embryo pickle; to his little daughter, three crocodile's eggs, and his humming-bird's nest upon the birth of the first child if she married with her mother's consent. His oldest son was cut off with a single-cockle-shell, but his second son he made his sole executor and heir of his "flowers, plants, minerals, shells, pebbles, fossils, beetles, butterflies, caterpillars, grasshoppers and vermin not previously specified," and also all his "monsters, both wet and dry." (*Tatler*, No. 216.) Addison had been reading the Fellows' papers as well as visiting the Society's repository!

In a paper in the *Spectator* (No. 21), the next year Addison expressed his concern about what he considered the over-stocking of the three great professions, divinity, law and physic, and the importance of entering trade. He recounts the maxim, "that when a nation abounds in physicians, it grows thin of people" and speaks of the physicians as a body of men "like the British army in Caesar's time . . . Some of them slay in chariots, and some on foot." Then he refers to the "retainers to physicians, who, for want of other patients, amuse themselves with the stifling of cats in an airpump, cutting up dogs alive, or impaling insects upon the point of a needle for microscopical observations; besides those that are employed in the gathering of weeds, and the chase of butterflies; not to mention the cockle-shell merchants and spider catchers."

Addison himself was interested in the microscope and knew of the observations the Dutch Leeuwenhoek was reporting to the Society and those that others were making during these years. So he recorded,—*Tatler*, No. 119,—a dreamed discourse by a good genius who said: "Your microscopes bring to sight shoals of living creatures in a spoonful of vinegar . . . You have often seen a dog opened to observe the circulation of the blood, or make any other useful inquiry; and yet would be tempted to laugh if I should tell you, that a circle of much greater philosophers than any of the Royal Society were present at the cutting up of one of these little animals which we find in the blue of a plum; that it was tied down alive before them; and that they observed the palpitations of the heart, the course of the blood, the working of the muscles and the convulsions in the several limbs with great accuracy and improvement." Addison adds, "I take greater pleasure in considering the works of the creation in their immensity than in their minuteness,"—and his magnificent hymn (1712) beginning "The spacious firmament on high" was one of the results of this greater pleasure.

In another issue of the *Tatler*,—No. 221,—supposed to have been written by Addison, the widow Gimcrack writes a letter telling of her husband's becoming a virtuoso and asking about the disposal of his estate. The first indication or symptom she noted was about fifteen years ago when he ordered the dismissal of an old weeding-woman because "there is no such thing in nature as a weed, and it was his design to let the garden produce what it pleased." His death from a fever had come after he had run after an odd-colored butterfly for some five miles. On his death-bed he had made his will, saying he would follow the Roman custom and release his slaves. "He ordered me to bring him a flea which he had kept for several months in a chain with a design, as he said, to give it its manumission. This was done accordingly." Now his widow offers bargains in a parcel of dried spiders for a penny-worth and also in cockle-shells, and asks if it is "best to sell my beetles in a lump, or by retail."

Addison's use of Sir Nicholas Gimcrack is proof of the vitality of Shadwell's creation many years earlier, just as Gimcrack's collections reflect the special interest of the amateurs in natural history. Among these naturalists Hans Sloane was one of the most conspicuous, as will appear later.

Gulliver's Travels

Swift, too, joined the writers who ridiculed the Society and its activities. The very setting of *Gulliver's Travels* (1726) mirrored the travellers' accounts popular with the Society in those years. Each of Gulliver's voyages satirized some phase of English contemporary life, the third one in particular, "The Voyage to Laputa," being the one most concerned with science. Swift's method has been described as that of simple imitation with the addition of a flourish of his own, with nonsense at the end, with the combination of two experiments in one, or with tenuous speculation presented as fact.[5] The Grand Academy of projectors of Lagado, which Swift described in the third *Voyage,* in its physical appearance resembles more probably the new government buildings being erected at this time along Whitehall than it does the Crane Court house of the Royal Society, though Swift had visited the Crane Court rooms soon after the Society had moved there. At the same time while Swift drew heavily on Boyle's works, published in complete form the year before, and on the *Philosophical Transactions,* yet he called his thinkers "projectors" and their schemes "projects," not "virtuosi" and "experiments." His terms were those of the speculative mania of that time, the promoters of the get-rich-quick schemes who sold shares to all comers, as the members of the Grand Academy begged for money "from all who go to see them." The "projects" themselves were based on actual accounts but presented "text without context."

A man at the Grand Academy sought to extract sunbeams from cucumbers to be placed in vials and released as needed,—and the studies of Grew, Boyle, Hooke, Hales and others on plant respiration were brought to the readers' mind. A blind man mixing colors by feeling and smelling "much encouraged by the whole fraternity" reflected Dr. Finch's report to Boyle of a blind man in the Low Countries who could at certain times distinguish colors by the touch of his fingers, and Boyle's suggestion that perhaps he could smell the dyes. The Laputan mathematicians and philosophers were contriving new rules and methods of agriculture and building, and new tools for all trades and manufactures . . . "but none of the projects are yet brought to perfection and in the meantime the whole country lies in waste."

5 S. J. Gould. Gulliver and the moons of Mars. *Jour. of the Hist. of Ideas,* VI (January, 1945) 91.

Swift's denunciation of the government and the leaders of his day in scientific as well as in political life were not shots in the dark, for a contemporary of his wrote: "However wild the description of . . . the manners and various projects . . . yet it is a real picture embellished with much latent wit and humor . . . It is a satire upon those astronomers and mathematicians who have so entirely dedicated their time to the planets, that they have been careless of their family and country, and have been chiefly anxious about the economy and welfare of the upper world." [6] Halley must have writhed, Flamsteed and other astronomers and mathematicians must have turned in their graves, but Newton was probably too old to care.

Swift too had not forgotten the Society's collections, and Gulliver, in the land of the Brobdingnags during his second Voyage, slew four wasps as big as partridges, cut out their stings which were $1\frac{1}{2}$ inches long and as sharp as needles and carefully preserved them. Upon his return to England, "I gave three of them to Gresham College and kept the fourth for myself." Evidently the move to Crane Court some fifteen years earlier did not prevent Swift's readers from recognizing the Royal Society in the reference to Gresham College. The interchangeable use of the names still persisted.

When Newton died and Sir Hans Sloane succeeded him in the presidency, Sir Hans took office in a Society that had grown half again as large as it had been twenty-four years earlier at Newton's coming. The foreign members had increased from about thirty to around seventy. Instead of an average of nine new members a year, as in the last decades of the preceding century, an average of fifteen were joining each year. The Society owned its own home and, regardless of the critics, it had an assured permanence, a stability that gave it an opportunity to develop. Under Sir Hans it did just that, even though certain weaknesses continued to invite ridicule before they were reformed.

---

[6] Cited in Nicolson, M. and Mohler, N., Scientific background of Swift's "Voyage to Laputa." *Annals of Science* II, No. 3 (July 1937), 334.

8

TARGETS FOR SATIRE

OR SIXTY-THREE YEARS Hans Sloane (1660-
1753) was connected with the Society in one position
or another. As a councilor and a secretary he had already begun important administrative improvements before Newton had moved to London. He worked closely
with Newton during the latter's presidency, and after the
latter's death was at once in his turn elected president and
continuously re-elected until he resigned in 1741. He remained on the Council, however, until his death twelve
years later.

In his youth Sloane had studied botany in Paris, as well
as medicine at Montpellier. A friend of Boyle and also of
John Ray, the great English naturalist, and a Fellow since
1685, he had made large collections of natural history
specimens in Jamaica where he had gone as physician to
the ducal governor for some fifteen months. Upon his return to London, while rapidly building up his medical
practice, he prepared and published his *Catalogue Plantarum* (1696) for Jamaica and followed this some years

later with volumes on his voyages there, to other islands in the West Indies and to Madeira. Meanwhile Oxford granted him his M.D. in 1701. Queen Anne called upon his professional services. George I created him a baronet in 1716 and appointed him physician-general to the army in 1722. George II made him his own first physician a few years later. He was also active in the Royal College of Physicians of which he had been made a fellow in 1687, serving as its president for sixteen years,—for many of which he was also president of the Royal Society.

His house in Bloomsbury was a center of hospitality as well as of books and of specimens, and he had also a manor in Chelsea which he bought late in Anne's reign. There he established a botanical garden and to this manor he retired in 1741. At both his homes, his library and his collections were freely available to his learned friends and visitors. Not every one of his contemporaries appreciated these collections, however. Edward Young, the poet who wrote *Night Thoughts,* in a collection of satires under the title of *Love of Fame, the Universal Passion* first published in the seventeen-twenties, wrote:

> But what in oddness can be more sublime
> Than Sloane, the foremost toyman of his time?
> His nice ambition lies in curious fancies;
> His daughter's portion a rich shell inhances,
> And Ashmole's baby-house, is in his view,
> Britannia's golden mine, a rich Peru!
> How his eyes languish! How his thoughts adore
> That painted coat, which Joseph never wore!
> He shows, on holidays, a sacred pin,
> That touched the ruff, that touch'd Queen Bess's chin.
> "Since that great dearth our chronicles deplore,
> Since that great plague that swept as many more,
> Was ever year unblest as this?" he'll cry,
> "It has not brought us one new butterfly."   (IV)

When Sir Hans died, he left his gardens to the Society of Apothecaries which he had established thirty years earlier, with the proviso that if they were not accepted, they were to go to the Royal College of Physicians and to the Royal Society jointly. His magnificent collections he left to the nation, if the government would pay his family £20,000, a fraction of their value. These included 40,000 books and some 3500 manuscripts as well as nearly 80,000 specimens of all kinds. (No wonder Young had called him "the foremost toyman of his time.") With the acceptance of these collections in 1754 and their removal to Montague House by the trustees for the government, to be combined with the Cotton Library and the Harleian MSS., the foundations of the British Museum were laid. For that first group of trustees, the government appointed the president of the Royal Society ex officio and nine of the members of the Council. And the president of the Society by virtue of his office has ever since continued to serve as a trustee for the Museum.

Dr. Sloane as Secretary

Dr. Sloane was secretary of the Royal Society from 1693 to 1712. With the aid of his fellow secretary, Richard Waller, a zoologist, he proceeded to bring order into the administration of the affairs of the Society, still in a precarious state. He insisted that the *Philosophical Transactions,* suspended between 1687 and 1691, be published regularly and he himself served as their editor for sixteen years. One result of the interruption in their publication for three years was that their circulation outside Britain had been seriously curtailed. The wars of these twenty years between England and France were a further interference with normal communication.

In spite of the wars, not only did Sloane revive Oldenburg's custom of inviting foreign correspondence, but he also took pains to send copies, and even sets, of the *Transactions* abroad, especially to his friends in France. He helped the librarian of the *Bibliothèque Royale* fill in the missing volumes in the set there, besides sending many other English books of scientific interest to that library. In the midst of the war, he was elected in 1709 to foreign membership in the *Académie des Sciences,* and in his turn recommended Frenchmen to membership in the Royal Society. After the war had ended, at least temporarily, there were some twenty of these French Fellows whose candidacies Sloane sponsored,—most of them while he was president,—among them Maupertuis and Réaumur, Buffon and Montesquieu.

As secretary, Sloane succeeded so well in restoring the financial well-being of the Society that by 1697 it was able to increase its investments. He was not satisfied, however, and pushed the Council into a long series of meetings to plan ways to improve matters further. Not till after he was himself president did he succeed in enforcing by legal process the obligation to pay the fees required of every candidate by bond after 1674, and too often disregarded. In the interim, the Society was often so handicapped financially that it did not have the money to pay the honoraria of its officers but would sometimes make gifts to them instead, as a remission of fees, or a number of copies of a book it had published. Waller and Sloane, both well to do, served without pay.

The Presidency of Sir Hans Sloane

During the fourteen years of Sloane's presidency three important innovations were made. Foreign members were exempted from paying subscriptions on the ground that their position was wholly honorary. Candidates required nomination by no less than three supporters over their own signatures. Fellows not meeting their financial obligations to the Society were to be sued if necessary. As a result of this third innovation, the treasury filled up rapidly as arrears in dues were paid.

In 1732 the Council was able to purchase for £1600 lands in Acton on the outskirts of the London of that day.

One hundred and fifty years later when the Society's activities had outgrown its ordinary receipts and finances for administration were again a problem, these lands, needed for building purposes, were sold for more than £32,000. The income from this capital helped the Society over a difficult time in the eighteen-seventies. Imagine Sir Hans Sloane's astonishment could he have seen this outcome of the purchase made during his administration!

The various reforms of course strengthened the framework of the Society and helped to attract supporters. The membership rolls rose rapidly; in 1740 at the close of Sloane's presidency, the Fellows numbered 301. But still the non-scientific members outnumbered the scientific ones by two to one.

During these years of Newton's and Sloane's rule, the mathematicians and astronomers as well as the doctors and the naturalists among the Fellows continued their scientific work. Halley succeeded Flamsteed as Astronomer Royal, to be followed after his death by James Bradley who had discovered the aberration of light. Stephen Hales was not only interested in Newtonian physics but also in animal and vegetable physiology, and then in the application of science to hygiene, ventilation and the purification of water and the preservation of foods. The long voyages of those days needed just such help to which Dr. James Lind also contributed in 1753 by his treatise on scurvy.

Some among the physicians and surgeons—the largest group among the scientist Fellows even as late as 1860—including Sir Hans Sloane were greatly interested during this period in the use of inoculation for the control of smallpox. The practice had become fashionable through the efforts of Lady Mary Wortley Montagu, with the aid of the court, after her return from Turkey where she had seen it used. A number of papers in favor of inoculation were published in the *Philosophical Transactions* and two large folio volumes of manuscripts on the statistics of the subject still remain in the Society's Library, as both Weld and Lyons report.

Studies of the weather—meteorology—had concerned the Fellows from the earliest days. Now it was proposed that the Society should help competent observers by furnishing them with the improved instruments available, such as thermometers, barometers, pendulum watches, and so forth. For Newton had invented the reflecting telescope by using a concave mirror for the convex lens of the refracting instrument. Dollond's discovery of the achromatic lens in 1758 was a long step forward towards its later perfecting. Fahrenheit had adopted the melting point of ice and the boiling point of water as fixed points of a scale for measuring temperatures and the values of 32°F. and 212°F. were respectively assigned, making thermometers at last useful instruments.

After Newton's death, however, under Sir Hans Sloane and his successors in office, many of the papers and studies presented to the Society tended to become more or less academic and some were downright trivial. Sloane himself has recently been characterized as both a snob and a dilettante.[1] Still, useful work went on and increasingly the government was turning to the Society for advice in connection with perplexing scientific matters. Parliament in 1714 had offered a reward to anyone who would devise a satisfactory method of obtaining an accurate determination of longitude at sea—a problem troubling the Fellows from their earliest days, as "The Ballad of Gresham College" reflects,—and had established a Board of Longitude with the Society's president as one of the Commissioners. During the next decades much work was done on the question; even Sir Christopher Wren in his old age worked at it.[2] The series of chronometers devised by John Harrison finally solved the problem, winning for him the Copley Medal from the Society in 1749, and on recommendation from the Council a number of grants from the government totaling £15,000.

[1] By C. E. Raven. *John Ray, Naturalist* (Cambridge, 1942), 336.
[2] *Parentalia*, 247, 346.

The Copley Medal

The establishment of the Copley Medal, incidentally, belongs to this period also. This, the highest distinction that the Royal Society has to bestow, originated in a legacy received in 1709. At first the interest from the one hundred pounds was used for experiments presented before the Society by its curator. Then in 1736 the suggestion was made that, instead, "a medal or other honorary prize should be bestowed on the person whose experiment should be best approved, by which means . . . a laudable emulation might be excited among men of genius to try their invention, who, in all probability, may never be moved for the sake of lucre." The awards were to be made by the two trustees of Sir Godfrey Copley's will, one of whom was Sir Hans Sloane. After Sloane's death in 1753, the nomination was made by the president and the Council. At that time also, the restriction was removed that limited the award to those of British nationality.

Since 1831 the Copley Medal has been awarded to the "living author of such philosophical research, either published or communicated to the Society, as may appear to the Council to be deserving of that honor." An additional gift from the Copley family in 1881 provided for a bonus to accompany the Medal, a gift now amounting to £35. With few exceptions since the seventeen-thirties, the Copley Medal has been awarded annually. The roll of the two hundred and more recipients of this Medal as the *Record* presents it is a proud one, ranging from men like Hales, Benjamin Franklin, Priestley, Cook, Herschel, Hunter, and Volta in the eighteenth century to Pavlov, Einstein, Sir William Bragg and Niels Bohr in the twentieth.

In the eighteenth century, however, by no means all the Fellows were concerned with science. Indeed, after Sloane's death, the men of science among the officers of the Society dwindled. In ten different years there was none at all.[3] Antiquarians, historians, librarians, there were aplenty. The Society of Antiquarians had been formed in 1717 and was incorporated in 1751. Many of its members were Fellows also and held office in the Society. Three of the six presidents in the thirty-year period between Sloane and Banks are listed as antiquarians in the *Record*. To one antiquary, the Reverend Thomas Birch, who was a secretary of the Society for thirteen years, scholars today are deeply indebted. He it was who transcribed and published the minutes of the Society from its first days through December, 1687.

Other Fellows were writers in various fields, or leaders in public affairs, but not men of science; for the Society had regained the prestige and the social prominence that led many to hope for election to membership because of the distinction F.R.S. after their names would give them.

John Hill versus the Society

Among these would-be candidates was John Hill, a man who failed to be elected, but who rendered the Society a signal service by causing it to revise its publications in answer to his ridicule of them. Hill ran a shop in London as an apothecary; but he also had a flowing pen, publishing some seventy-odd poems, operas, plays and novels, scientific and pseudo-scientific papers. His translation of Theophrastus' *On Gems* won him public recognition and he hoped with that and the two papers of his published in the *Philosophical Transactions* to win election. At the same time, however, in his newspaper writing he was poking endless fun at the antiquarians, calling them "medal-scrapers" and "antediluvian knife-scrapers," while the scientific collectors he termed "cockleshell merchants," and the naturalists "recorders of histories of stickle-backs and

3 Lyons, 163.

cockchafers." These jests proved expensive for no three Fellows would sign Hill's nomination for membership in the Society.[4] So he took his revenge.

His most effective production was *A Review of the Works of the Royal Society of London: containing animadversions on such of the Papers as deserve Particular Observation* (1751). This he dedicated to the president of the Society, with bitter sarcasm, holding him directly responsible for the charges he made. In the preface, Hill stated that he had been criticized for assuming to know more than the Society and added "surely a man may do that, and yet be very ignorant." He hoped that his work would be of use in establishing truth, in contrast to what the Society—"the Grand Champion of Errors"—had published, and "that the Society may by means of it become ashamed of what it has been and that the World may know he is not a member of it, till it is an Honour to a man to become so." As a final thrust he concluded his preface with Steele's paragraph from the *Tatler* already quoted (p. 127).

He selected and edited "the more trivial and downright foolish articles" which appeared in the *Transactions* from the first issue on through the contemporary ones, and "underlined in his own words their absurdities." He divided his papers under the headings of arts, antiquities, medicine, miracles, zoophytes, animals, vegetables, and minerals. "A Way to kill Rattlesnakes" was compared with a way to kill fleas. There were papers on a merman (based on a contribution from Cotton Mather), on the unicorn's horn, on the transmutation of water into maggots, and "incontestable proofs of a strange and surprising Fact, namely, that Fish will live in Water." The lack of discrimination on the part of the editor of the *Transactions* was his major target, one which he made painfully clear. At the same time, he showed his own common sense and his own fund of knowledge as he scored the obvious and

4 D'Israeli, I. *Calamities and Quarrels of Authors*, ed. by his son (London, n.d.) II, 364-5.

the incomplete observations, the obscure terms and the faulty logic of the arguments.

Two of the shorter papers from the *Review* illustrate these comments. One, from Part III "on Medical Cases described in the Transactions" is the fifth chapter:

A miraculous Cure for Fresh Wounds

This is a Remedy taken from the Vegetable World; it is published in the hundred and seventeenth Number of the Philosophical Transactions, and the World is obliged to that ever memorable Knight Sir *George Mackenzie* for it. It was discovered to him in the Way of most of the old Physick of the World, according to some Authors, that is, by the Brutes. The Plant is the *Lancashire* Asphodell, the *Asphodelus Lancastriae Verus* of *Johnson,* as Sir *George* says, tho' he tells us it grows in Forests, and *Johnson* makes it an inhabitant only of rotten Morasses; this however is of small Consequence, be the Plant what it will, or grow where it will, its Effects are sufficiently ascertained, and these are all a *Royal Society* need take any care about. He says, it is so miraculous a Vulnerary, that but to touch it, is to be healed; and for Conviction, assures us, that the Deer, when wounded, only run to this Plant, and lie down upon it, in order to cure themselves. Sir *George,* not above learning from the Brute Creation, made a salve with the Herb with Butter and Wax, which he tells had no Fault, but that it healed a Wound too quickly. Ought not one to suspect from this, that Sir *George* was a Surgeon?

We are vastly apt to suspect two Things, in regard to this Miraculous Matter; the one is, that Sir *George,* or somebody for him, stole this Account of its Virtues on the Deer, from the old Story of the Goats of *Mount Ida,* curing themselves of their Wounds by the Dittany that grows there; the other, that if ever the Ointment mentioned was made, the Wax and Butter had more Effect in the Cure than the Asphodell.

The other paper is the second chapter of Part VI, Book IV "of Animals":

Of the Manner in which Reptiles change or cast their Skins.

It seems impossible to be of the Name of *Baker,* and not to be a Philosopher: The Author of this curious Dissertation is a Son of the Gentleman of that Name, so often and so justly celebrated in this Work. It stands in the four hundred and eighty-third Number of the Philosophical Transactions.

This young Gentleman, after taking up somewhat too much Paper in telling us, that the Water-Newt changes or casts its Skin as Serpents do, and communicating some other Observations of equal Consequence, observes, that the Reason of his troubling the *Royal Society* with this Relation is, that tho' it has been long known, that the Serpent Kind cast their Skins, yet we are ignorant of the Manner of their doing it, because they do it in their Holes; but that by knowing how this of the Newt is done, we may form a reasonable Guess at the Way in which the others perform it.

He tells us, that the Newt gets its Skin off by loosening *with its fore Feet* the Skin about the Jaws, and getting first one Leg and then the other of this Pair out, after which the rest is easy: And who will doubt, but that this must convey a very distinct Idea of the Manner in which Serpents do it, which have no Feet at all.

The Youth of this little Philosopher pleads against our saying any more: We are not censuring him for writing, but the President of the *Royal Society* for countenancing such Matters.

Such satire was not new. A certain Dr. King, with a degree in civil law, a friend of Swift's, had with a rare sense of humor taken many a shot at the *Transactions* before, and also at Sloane's not impeccable English in some of those papers. (Sloane as secretary acted as editor of the *Philosophical Transactions* from 1695 to 1713.) Sloane, for instance, had given an account of a "child born without a brain." "Had it lived long enough," remarked King, "it would have made an excellent publisher of *Philosophical Transactions!*" [5]

Hill's method was, by combining a humor like King's with a knowledge like Stubbs', to make the reader aware that the papers burlesqued had not the slightest scientific value, or else added nothing to previously known observations or theory. And D'Israeli has long since pointed out that there was no inconsiderable knowledge on Hill's

[5] D'Israeli, *op. cit.* II 358-360 and note, 363.

part interspersed with the ridicule. What Hill accomplished may be inferred by the fact that in 1751-2 the Council took the editing of the *Philosophical Transactions* out of the hands of the secretary, Dr. Cromwell Mortimer, who had been in charge since 1730, and placed the responsibility for it in the hands of a committee. D'Israeli's comment was that Hill did more for the improvement of the *Philosophical Transactions* than did any other contemporary.

That Hill's barbs struck home and that the Society winced under his attacks seems clear from the *Advertisement* which still precedes each volume of the *Philosophical Transactions* almost two hundred years later. In it the Society states that until the 47th volume, the printing of the *Transactions* had been "the single act of the respective secretaries." The Society as a body had not concerned itself further except by occasionally recommending their revival when they had been intermitted. This was done, the *Advertisement* states, principally to satisfy the public that the usual meetings were continuing. With the growth of the Society "lately" and the increase in the number of communications, a committee had been set up March 26, 1752, to read and select the papers for publication, but they were not answerable "for the certainty of the facts" nor for "the propriety of the reasonings." It was an established rule of the Society never to give opinions as a body upon any subject either of Nature or Art. Therefore the thanks proposed from the chair for a speech or a book was merely a matter of civility. This held true also for any projects, inventions and curiosities exhibited, even though their demonstrators might report that they had met with "highest applause and approbation." "It is hoped that no regard will hereafter be paid to such reports and public notices; which in some instances have been too lightly credited, to the dishonour of the Society." Thus the Society answered Hill.

Hill's egotism survived undiminished all the quarrels and antagonisms he provoked—and they were many—but

PLATE 12. The Honorable Robert Boyle

(From *The Record of the Royal Society*, London, 1940, by courtesy of the Royal Society)

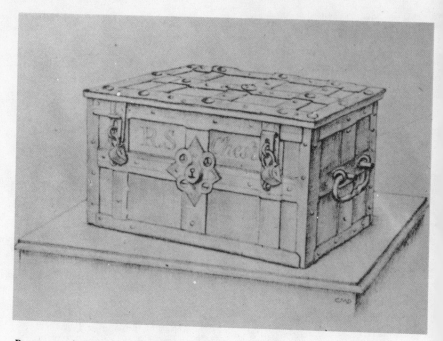

PLATE 13. A Drawing of the iron-bound Treasurer's Chest with its three locks presented to the Royal Society in 1663

(From *The Record of the Royal Society*, London, 1940, by courtesy of the Royal Society)

it is hard to understand today how a man such as he, after his affronts to the Society and to Sloane, should have publicly advertised himself in his newspaper articles as "the properest person" to be placed in charge of the Sloane collections when the government took them over two or three years later.

"That foreigners will resort to this collection is certain, for it is the most considerable in the world; and that our own people will often visit it is as sure, because it may be made the means of much useful as well as curious knowledge. One and the other will expect a person in that office who has sufficient knowledge: he must be able to give an account of every article, freely and fluently, not only in his own, but in the Latin and French languages.

"This the world . . . sees is not a place that any one can execute: it requires knowledge in a peculiar and uncommon kind of study—knowledge which very few possess; and in which . . . the bitterest of my enemies (and I have thousands, although neither myself nor they know why) will not say I am deficient . . .

"What are my own abilities it very ill becomes me thus to boast; but did they not qualify me for the trust . . . I would not ask it. As to those of any other, unless a man be conjured from the dead, I shall not fear to say there is not any one whoever that is able so much as to call the parts of the collection by their names . . .

"Many excel . . . in other studies; it is my chance to have bestowed the labour of my life on this: those labours may be of some use to others . . ." [6]

Suffice it to say, Hill did not receive the appointment. Through the influence of Lord Bute he did become connected with the Royal Gardens at Kew. His main achievement, the publication of which ruined him financially, was twenty-six folio volumes on his *Vegetable System,* containing 1600 plates illustrating 26,000 different plants. By his genuine ability in this field he helped to spread a more general interest in botany.

[6] Cited by D'Israeli, *op. cit.* II, 373-374 note.

As far as the Royal Society was concerned, though his scientific work was done without the F.R.S., Hill's service to the Society was important. By his critical satires he had brought to light a serious weakness in the Society's main activity, the futility of many of the papers presented to it and accepted for publication. Reform in the selection of the papers to be printed carried with it improvement in the quality of the papers presented before the Society. A threatened subsidence into complete triviality and puerility in the Society's major work was finally checked. Again the Society had weathered a dangerous period in its history.

Thereafter, also, the *Philosophical Transactions* was the better able to serve scientists by giving their researches widespread publicity through its pages. Little if anything of major importance in the scientific world during these centuries has failed to be recorded therein, a service so valuable that late in the nineteenth century it was claimed that were all scientific literature destroyed except the *Transactions,* science would not have suffered an irreparable loss. For in the *Transactions* would be preserved all work of importance. Whether or not this claim was valid, its assertion highlights the outstanding usefulness of the *Transactions* to science.

9

CONTACTS OVERSEAS*

A BREAK in the strictly chronological sequence of
events seems appropriate at this point to present
two aspects of the Society's affairs. One is a consideration of the Society's changing procedures in connection with its selection of members, the other, a swift survey of its selection of Americans as Fellows through the
years.

If the Royal Society was to become a scientific association, the change would have to come through the election
of properly qualified members. The eighteenth century
provided the procedures necessary, after earlier experience
had made clear the disadvantages of non-selective admissions; but the application of these procedures depended
upon the Council. Not until scientists were in the majority
on that powerful group of twenty-one men, could the procedures be successfully applied. As that did not happen

---

* See Bibliography and Sources, Chapter 9. Attention should be called to
the valuable article on colonial Fellows published after this chapter was
completed. Denny, M. The Royal Society and American scholars. *Scientific
Monthly*, vol. 65, no. 5 (November 1947) 415-427.

until the nineteenth century, the Society continued to be mainly an association of science-lovers, of amateurs, with a growing resemblance to a fashionable men's club.

Linked inextricably with this problem of a qualified membership was the one of finances, for it must always be remembered that the Society through these years received no subsidy from the government and later received only its housing rent-free. It was solely dependent upon membership fees, gifts and legacies. Gifts and legacies were slow in coming in and membership fees were too often in arrears. The Society's financial situation was a continual concern to its Council until the late nineteenth century. Procedures of election to membership had therefore a twofold importance.

Election Procedures

The original plan (1663) provided that a candidate could be proposed at one meeting of the Society, and be balloted for at a subsequent meeting if a quorum were present. He then became a Fellow upon signing the obligation to support the work by his presence and by the payment of the weekly shilling. This was to be done within four weeks after his election when the candidate, after paying his admission fee of forty shillings, was received formally into the Society by the president.

The following year the Council added a provision that anyone living in foreign parts, after having been duly elected, should be registered among the Fellows without having to make these payments and without going through the usual appearance in person to be formally accepted. Certification of his election under the Society's seal would be sent him. These statutes were then extended to cover colonials as well as foreign members, making it unnecessary for any of them, while residing abroad, to pay the weekly fees. Ten years later the Council provided further that Fellows absent from England for more than three months were released from similar payments until they had returned home. These measures proved too lax and the finances of the Society suffered severely.

The first important corrections of the situation were made during the presidency of Sir Christopher Wren in the critical period. Some years before, in August, 1674, as the Society was slowing down after the excitement of its first decade, the Council had set as its policy: "To make the Society prosper, good experiments must be in the first place provided, to make the weekly meetings considerable, and that the expenses for making these experiments must be secured by legal subscriptions for paying the contributions; which being done, the Council might then with confidence proceed to the ejection of useless members."

With Sir Christopher's firm guidance, the Council now required that hereafter it must first pass upon the name of a proposed candidate. Only if the Council thought that the candidate might be useful to the Society, would his name be presented at the next meeting and be balloted on according to the statutes. Also, the candidate was to sign a bond, an obligation, for the payment of the dues. Other modifications were made later; but these two have remained unchanged,—the Council's control over nominations and the candidate's obligation to pay (though now for more than a hundred years he has not had to sign a note).

This control by the Council over nominations to membership was fundamental; for by it the Council could determine the character of the Society as well as its size. How important this power was—and is—will be made still more apparent when the reforms of the nineteenth century are considered later. Meantime, until 1753 when all these remissions of fees were cancelled, English residents abroad as well as foreigners and colonials, continued to be exempt from the formal subscription, the ceremonial admission and the payments of the weekly shillings. (Later, an alternative payment of £21 was permitted.) Colonials at no time could vote, however, until they had come to London and been formally admitted.

When Cotton Mather wrote from Boston in 1712 that he was sending a small collection of curiosities from America to the Society and would be glad to write annually on appropriate subjects, he added that he would welcome election to membership, agreeing in advance to support the purposes of the Society. The next year, Waller the secretary proposed his name, the Council approved, and according to Waller's letter to Mather, the Society admitted him; but it left his name as a non-voter out of the printed lists prepared for the use of the Fellows resident in England and participating in the annual elections. Existing minutes of the Society do not record that election, and when Mather's associates in America questioned his use of the F.R.S., not finding his name on the printed lists, one of them wrote to the Society desiring a certificate whether or no Mather was truly a Fellow. Finding no record of a vote having been taken, in 1723 the Society formally elected him, though today the Society lists Cotton Mather as elected a Fellow in July, 1713.

Under Sloane's presidency a few years later, because of Mather's difficulties, fellowship for the non-residents was defined as beginning when the election had been registered in the journal-book. They would be non-voters until they had qualified by appearing personally at the Society when they first came to London thereafter. Fifty years after the Council under Wren had set up the first controls, under Sloane's guidance another step was taken. After 1730 every candidate must be proposed by three or more members in written statements over their own signatures. (Nowadays at least six such endorsements are required.) These statements or certificates, to be filed with the secretary, were to give the candidates' occupations, their chief qualifications, their inventions, discoveries, works or writings, as well as their names and addresses. If the Council approved them, these papers were then to be posted for ten or more meetings of the Society before the ballot would be taken. The only exceptions were for those of royal blood, peers, the sons of peers, privy coun-

cilors and foreign princes or ambassadors; these could be
proposed by any individual and elected on the same day.
Rather amusingly, the Council soon had to rule that the
signers of these certificates should have personal knowledge of their nominees!

Had the Council then carefully considered and controlled these certificates of nomination, the Royal Society
might indeed have become a scientific body a hundred
years before that was actually accomplished. Since the
Council failed to do this, the non-scientists continued to
out-number the scientists by about two to one and the
antiquarians, historians, and "gentlemen" of wealth and
title continued in control.

Colonial American Fellows

Such were the procedures by which colonial Americans
as well as foreigners were welcomed into the Society. Colonial Americans, it should be remembered, were those
who were making their homes in the British colonies overseas, though many of them might have relatives or business
in the British Isles that would bring them back for visits
of varying lengths. These colonials are to be differentiated
from the Britishers who went out to the colonies on government business or as visitors, returning afterwards to
England to live. Until the Revolution released the colonials from their allegiance to the Crown, they were in a
kind of special category of membership in the Royal Society, as they were obviously not foreigners nor were they
voting members until they had come to London and been
formally admitted in person.

From the formation of the Society until the American
Revolution was over, there were some twenty notable
colonial Fellows. Like most of their British associates, they
were important men of affairs or of the learned professions,—doctors, clergymen, lawyers,—for whom scientific
pursuits were a side interest rather than a main activity.

Only two or three of them were professors of "natural philosophy" or of mathematics. But they were all interested in the natural world about them; they enjoyed reading, observing, experimenting, collecting as they had time and opportunity. Naturally, like Cotton Mather, they wanted to keep in touch with people of similar interests through the Society as a kind of clearing-house for contemporary scientific news. Cotton Mather's case also illustrates the probable distinction that election to membership in the London organization might confer in the colonies. In general, however, only those colonials who came to London themselves or who had powerful friends there to make known among the Fellows their publications and their scientific interests would be likely to attract attention. So it is not strange that in the course of the years till 1788 there were only about a score of these colonial Fellows.

A glance through the list of names illustrates these comments, though it is not always clear whether a man was elected as a colonial temporarily in London or as a Briton with experience in the colonies who has returned to England as a permanent resident. Governor John Winthrop of Connecticut, as has been pointed out earlier, joined the Society in its infancy, becoming an Original Fellow. He kept up active correspondence with it until his death in 1676. The next to be elected was William Penn, under Wren's presidency in 1681. He presented the Society with a map of "Pennsilvania" on that occasion. William Byrd of Virginia was elected next, in 1696 after he had been a guest at various meetings. He was able to attend the meetings frequently during the next few years and was twice elected to membership on the Council. Upon his return to Virginia until his death in 1744 he sent back letters and curiosities from that colony.

The fourth of these American colonials and the first Fellow to have been born in the colonies was Cotton Mather, whose unrecorded election in 1713 caused such difficulties ten years later. Just before his election, the Society had

had read to it by the secretary some of Mather's communications "concerning some Plants, Observations on the Rattle-Snake, and of Rain-bows, with a Confirmation of what had formerly been communicated to the Society concerning the Changing of the Direction of a Magnetical Needle to the contrary Poles by a Storm of Thunder at Sea." From these the Fellows judged him "a very inquisitive and proper Person" with whom to have a correspondence.

Among the Britishers elected in part because of their experiences in the colonies were William Burnet, later governor of New York and New Jersey, and then of Massachusetts, and Francis Nicolson, lately governor of Maryland and of Virginia and soon to be governor of Nova Scotia and then of South Carolina. Both were elected in 1706. But these men were not colonials like Byrd and Mather; nor were the Fellows from the West Indies like Dr. Thomas Hoy of Jamaica and Colonel Walter Douglas, governor of the Leeward Islands. Their membership, however, and that of others from the British possessions in the New World, widened the contacts of the Society and channeled a diverse series of communications and curiosities into the Crane Court house.

Among the colonials, William Brattle, a clergyman of Cambridge, Massachusetts, apparently declined the honor of his election in 1713/14 as he held himself unqualified. (The Fellows had hoped through his election to secure the scientific papers of his brother Thomas, who had recently died and who had been one of their correspondents!) But John Leverett, president of Harvard College, and Elihu Yale, Boston-born philanthropist for whom Yale College was named, both accepted their elections. Three other Massachusetts science-lovers, Paul Dudley, naturalist and lawyer, Dr. Thomas Robie, a Harvard tutor, and Dr. Zabdiel Boylston, the famous physician, were elected before Newton's death. Mr. Dudley, as a naturalist, for twenty years sent to the Royal Society communications on scientific matters concerning New England. Dr. Boylston was elected while in England "to study the new method for cutting the Stone."

In the seventeen-thirties John Winthrop, grandson of the Original Fellow, having been a guest at the meetings and having made various gifts with promises of more, was deemed "a proper person" for election for he was "well skilled in Natural knowledge, and particularly in Chemistry." Soon thereafter he presented to the Society a collection of 364 items from New England, which was the largest single gift received up to that time. In recognition of it, the Society returned his bond and exempted him from all fees.

James Oglethorpe, founder of Savannah, Georgia, and chief supporter of Georgia in its early years, like Dr. John Mitchell of Virginia, was not elected to membership until after he had become a London resident. Oglethorpe was described as "well versed in Natural History, Mathematicks, and all branches of Polite Literature," while Dr. Mitchell had sent from Virginia "a very curious dissertation concerning the Colour of the skin in Negroes" and from his study of "Natural History, especially Botany," had become "very well acquainted with the Vegetable production of North America." Two others elected Fellows with similar scientific knowledge and colonial experience, were Henry Ellis, hydrographer and for three years governor of Georgia, and Francis Fauquier, lieutenant-governor of Virginia but actually its head for a decade or so. Fauquier was stated to be "a gentleman of great merit, well versed in Philosophical and Mathematical inquiries, and a great promoter of usefull Learning." Yet again these men were not American colonials like Dr. Boylston and Cotton Mather, even though their qualifications for membership as stated in the certificates by their sponsors often referred to their American experiences.

Robert Morris of New York, later governor of Pennsylvania, was a true colonial, however, and his presence in London in the early fifties led to his election then and to his formal admittance when he returned there some years later. He was chosen, it appears, as "a Gentleman studious of promoting Natural and Experimental Knowledge and of Communicating to this Society any curious or ~eful Observations that may arise within the said Province." A notable Philadelphian also elected was Dr. John Morgan, founder of the medical school of the University of Pennsylvania, medical director of the Continental Army, professor of medicine in the College of Philadelphia, and a "zealous Inquirer into Anatomical and Physiological Subjects." Though he sent his fees in full, apparently he never presented himself in person for the formal admission. Another physician, Dr. John Tennent of Virginia and New York, was in London in 1765 and therefore able to be formally admitted after his election that year. He had long been in correspondence with Sir Hans Sloane and other Fellows about medical botany.

Benjamin Franklin, elected in 1756, is the most famous of all these colonials. As more will be said about him later, only the fact of his election is noted here.

Nominated by Franklin and four others, and with his bond signed for him and his fees paid by Franklin, John Winthrop, professor of mathematics and "natural philosophy" at Harvard College, became a Fellow in 1767. Franklin did a similar service about the same time for Dr. Arthur Lee of Virginia,—a gentleman esteemed "for his Learning, Ingenuity and Knowledge in Natural Philosophy." But Dr. Lee was a lawyer and a publicist as well as a physician. With the establishment of American independence, he considered himself released from his obligations to the Royal Society—he had previously signed his own bond and Franklin's had been returned—and refused to heed the reminders sent him about his arrears in dues. Consequently in 1788 the Council accepted this as a resignation and canceled his membership.

Two loyalists who were elected during this period were Dr. Alexander Garden, the eminent naturalist of "Charles Town," South Carolina, and Peter Livius of New Hampshire, later chief justice of Canada. His gift of the horns of an American elk seems to have paved the way for Livius' election, although he too was "well versed in various branches of Science." Another American who came to England to stay just before the Revolution and became a Fellow in 1779, was Benjamin Thompson, better known as Count Rumford, the physicist and inventor. Seventeen years later he bestowed on the Society the Rumford Fund, the income from which was to provide the Rumford Medal for "the author of the most important discovery or useful improvement made public in any way during the two previous years on heat or on light, as would tend most to promote the good of mankind."

With the election to the list of foreign members in 1788 of James Bowdoin of Boston, governor of Massachusetts in 1785, one of the founders of the American Academy of Arts and Sciences in Boston and its first president, the Royal Society recognized American independence. Thereafter Americans were not colonials; they were foreigners.

Hindrances to Americans as Fellows

During this colonial period the Royal Society had welcomed into its fellowship leaders in American political and intellectual life, men most of whom were not primarily scientists but important men of affairs. The Society also had welcomed Londoners who had made names for themselves in the colonies through government service and whose recreation had been the promotion of natural knowledge. Through them and through the friends and relatives of these and other science-lovers, the Society had kept in close touch with the lands overseas from the days of the first Winthrop to the coming of the young Benjamin Thompson. The award of the Copley Medal to Franklin in 1753 was an ungrudging recognition of superior achievement by a colonial overseas.

These colonials in their turn welcomed contact with the Society. They offered to conduct regular correspondence, they sent specimens and they asked for election to membership. They tested their own studies and observations by the criticisms and experiments of their fellow science-lovers in London. And they followed their example by establishing their own American Philosophical Society and Academies of Arts and Sciences. Throughout the colonial period of American history, the Royal Society was in fairly close touch with American scientific work. But after the Revolution Americans became foreigners and American scientific pursuits, with few exceptions, developed more or less independently of the Society's interests, for the next half century or more.

The severance of the political tie was not the sole cause of this separation. The Society itself continued to suffer because of the non-scientific character of the majority of its members. In spite of the steps taken to make possible a more seriously scientific organization by requiring the Council's approval of nominees before their names could be balloted on, and the support of these nominations by a written statement of their qualifications, the Society remained an association of notables interested in science,— for the most part amateurs and patrons of science. Actually, as Lyons has pointed out, between 1740 and 1820, in ten different years not a single scientist was an officer of this supposedly scientific body, and in thirty-nine other years there was only one scientist among its officers.

The dominance of Sir Joseph Banks, president of the Society for more than forty years until his death in 1820, made increasingly difficult any check upon its weakness and stagnation during the early nineteenth century. When the reformers finally succeeded in bringing about the necessary changes, more years had to pass before these changes went into full effect. The story of these struggles will be told in later chapters. They are mentioned here, for they also serve to account for the curiously limited number of American Fellows elected during the first seventy-five years of the nineteenth century.

Americans were now foreigners, of course, and the Society attacked one aspect of its membership problems after Sir Joseph's death by deciding to restrict the number of foreign members. There had been as many as 161 of them in the seventeen-sixties. Sixty years later they were down to forty, and the Council held fifty to be an adequate number. That, too, helps to account for the shrinkage in the number of Americans in the list. But why should there have been only three elected between 1800 and 1861?

American Members on the Foreign List

It will be remembered that James Bowdoin in 1788 was the first American elected to foreign membership after the Revolution had ended. His election was followed seven years later by that of David Rittenhouse, Philadelphia's leading instrument-maker and astronomer.

Then in 1818 came that of Captain Bowditch, mathematician and astronomer whose *New American Practical Navigator* became the seaman's guide. Sir Joseph Banks, himself an old sailor and explorer, must have taken particular interest in his election.

After that there is a long gap in which three men with American connections, to be sure, are elected but not on the foreign list. Though David Hosack became one of New York's leading physicians, he was elected in 1816 to the ordinary fellowship, for he was the son of a Scot and had followed his American training with studies in Edinburgh and London and had read a paper on vision before the Royal Society while he was over there. James Audubon, the ornithologist, similarly was elected to the ordinary list in 1830, while Louis Agassiz, Harvard's great professor of natural science, was added to the foreign list as a Swiss, some years before he came to the United States.

After Bowditch in 1818, the first American to be elected to the foreign list was Benjamin Pierce, the Harvard mathematician, in 1852. He was followed nine years later by Alexander Bache, Franklin's great-grandson, a physicist who held many important positions before becoming regent of the Smithsonian Institution. Then again there were no American members until 1873 when Asa Gray, the botanist, received election.

Surely the three American members, Bowditch, Pierce and Bache, elected to the foreign list between 1800 and 1861, do not represent the total of American distinction in science during those decades. Where were Beaumont, Silliman and Dana, for instance?

It is true that Dr. William Beaumont, the army surgeon whose classic studies published in 1833 on the physiology of digestion as observed in the stomach of his patient, Alexis St. Martin, may have been too little known in those early days to gain him foreign recognition. But Benjamin Silliman's career at Yale University as professor of chemistry and geology,—"pathfinder in American science," as he has been called—must have been noted by the Fellows. For Silliman as a young man in 1805 had spent a year abroad and while in London, had breakfasted with Sir Joseph Banks, had attended sessions both of the Royal Society and of the Royal Institution, and had met some of the leading scientists of the day. With these London connections already established, it is the more surprising that his later achievements were not rewarded by election to the Fellowship.

His successor in 1856 as professor of geology, James Dwight Dana, had already published in 1837 a study of mineralogy that for sixty years was the standard classic in the field, widely acclaimed in Europe as well as in the United States. Dana's work as an explorer with the Wilkes expedition for four years in the Pacific regions ought also to have attracted the attention of the Society that had for so long been encouraging similar expeditions.

It was not that American science was unimportant, but that the Royal Society during these years was absorbed in its own difficulties. By 1873, however, the reorganization of the Royal Society into an association of scientists had begun to take effect.

Thereafter, elections of American scientists came at close intervals, and once, in 1919, five Americans were elected at one time. By 1938, there had been in all thirty-three of them among the foreign members, while five others had been elected in the ordinary or home classification as residents of Britain. In 1946 there were altogether fifteen Americans among the forty-seven living foreign members of that year.

10

CONSERVATISM

ENGLAND under its Hanoverian kings lived in an era of sharp contrasts. The old order died slowly for Toryism had penetrated many phases of its national life. The winds of revolution and reform were rising as the eighteenth century wore on, but they blew in gusts. In the lulls between, the established order continued in education as in politics, in science as in theology. Newton had lived on to the reign of the second of the Georges. Nearly a hundred years later, in 1820, Sir Joseph Banks and George III had both died. Then, after seventeen years, Queen Victoria ushered in a new age which already had made its approach felt.

The course of the Royal Society needs to be considered against the background of these changing times. It should also be noted that, while its Fellows were many of them prominent in public affairs, most of them belonged to the aristocracy either by birth or by virtue of their positions and affiliations. If Sloane was a snob, so also was Sir Joseph

Banks, the critics claimed. Weld wrote of Sir Humphry Davy's "inordinate admiration of hereditary rank." Even Dr. Granville, one of the Society's severest critics in the 1830's, declared that he had voted for the Royal Duke of Sussex as president in preference to his astronomer opponent, the younger Herschel, because the issue in that election as he saw it was: "Whether a Royal Prince, well known for his love and patronage of the arts and science, with an influence equal to his willingness to exert it on behalf of those who cultivate 'natural knowledge,' or a Philosopher of powerful talents and universal reputation, but without some of the many qualifications which were peculiar to the position in society of his illustrious competitor, was the most likely to benefit the learned body over which he was called to preside". . . . The Royal Society had indeed become a gentlemen's club by the late eighteenth century, seemingly unaffected by the winds of reform and equality that were blowing more and more strongly around it.

Wars and Their Consequences

The latter half of the eighteenth century was a turbulent time in English history, and an unhappy one; for the people were swept by smallpox, debased by gin-drinking, and oppressed by the increasing severity of the penalties for crimes. Always there were wars.

Great Britain under the Hanoverians was too closely involved in European questions and colonial rivalries to be for long at peace during this century. The great trading ships on the high seas sought to outdo their competitors or their ancient rivals. Smuggling was a virtue. In the forties the War of Jenkins' Ear merged into the War of the Austrian Succession. The return of peace brought only a return to the *status quo ante bellum* and shortly thereafter the greater Seven Years War of the midcentury embroiled the nations. Now as never before the struggle was being fought out in far countries as well as on the continent of

Europe,—in India and in Canada, on the Ohio River and on the St. Lawrence,—and on the high seas also.

The causes of the conflict were not just the continental rivalries of Hapsburg and Bourbon for a throne, but the century-long struggle between two great commercial and colonial powers, Britain and France, and their respective allies, for the control of vast undeveloped territories, for the wealth of the Indies, for the raw materials for manufacture, trade and export, and for the right to sail the high seas where they would. Thus during the eighteenth century, from the War of the Spanish Succession to the Napoleonic Wars, with few short intermissions, Britain and France were locked in fierce competition. In the process Britain lost her thirteen colonies on the Atlantic seaboard, but she won India and Canada and her captains discovered Australia for her as well.

Wars cost money as well as men. Government expenditures ran high; so taxes were levied on salt, windows, bricks, candles, newspapers, thus hindering the improvement of the people's condition. Newton's coinage in its turn was being debased or counterfeited. People counted their money by weight with pocket balances, to guard against chipped or light weight coins.

Yet this was the Age of Reason, of formal writing and of formal gardens. Statesmen and literary men, artists and inventors, scientists and philosophers gave it distinction. Addison and Steele in their essays had helped to lift literature out of the depravity of the Restoration era. Swift's satires, Dr. Johnson's *Dictionary*, Horace Walpole's letters, Fielding, Richardson, and Goldsmith in novels and poetry portrayed the period in writing just as Hogarth, Reynolds, Gainsborough, Raeburn and Romney did in art. Handel's music charmed the court while David Garrick and Mrs. Siddons won immortality on the stage. The eloquence of the contemporary French writers,—Voltaire, Montesquieu, Diderot, Rousseau, to name but a few—stirred, many of them, by the ferments arising from England's "century of genius," spread their ideas of liberty and reform far beyond the borders of France to stimulate political thinking and to train the minds of John Adams and Thomas Jefferson, Patrick Henry and many another leader of revolution in lands across the sea as well as at home.

This was the century when in England improvements in road-building enabled easier communication, and the building of canals facilitated commerce, while new devices in spinning and weaving increased the supply of cloth to be bought and sold. Kay's flying shuttle and the spinning jenny helped speed up production; but the demand for more wool to supply the cottage workers led to the enclosing of the ancient common lands and the dispossessing of the small farmers to provide more pasturage for larger flocks of sheep. The cry for more cotton from the New World was unceasing. The smelting of iron by coal, and the application of power, first water and then steam, to the looms producing the cloth, made the mining of coal more important. The miners dug deeper and the pumps worked harder to clear these mines of water. It would not be long before these stationary steam-driven pumping engines would be developed into the railway locomotives of the nineteenth century. And the Royal Society shared in many of these activities by welcoming the leaders into their membership and by publishing their ideas and repeating their experiments.

Population in England more than doubled. But the ill effects of the growing industrial revolution were already apparent as the workers shifted from the farms to the slums of the towns and cities. Soon the labor of women and children in the mills would be in demand, while the sturdy father and husband could find no work in the towns far from the farm from which he had been forced to move. By the end of the century the industrial revolution was in full tide, unchecked as yet, while the government pursued the let-alone policy advocated by Adam Smith and other economists of the day.

This same attitude of governmental indifference had allowed the colonies overseas to "flourish by neglect" throughout the greater part of the century, though far-seeing statesmen like the elder Pitt and later Fox and Burke might recognize their importance. Finally, the high cost of wars undertaken in part for the protection and defence of the colonies, seemed properly to be paid for at least in part through taxation of the colonists themselves. The American Revolution resulted, followed shortly by the French Revolution. By the end of the eighteenth century the age of revolution was shaking all the New World, both north and south, and the benevolent despots on European thrones found themselves confronted by popular strength and growing forces of nationalism which compelled both cruel suppression and grudging reform.

Education, Dissenters, and Science

Before we return to the Royal Society's activities during this tumultuous period, one additional aspect of the times should be mentioned. What was happening to education, especially as it affected science? The two universities after the upheavals in connection with the Civil War of the seventeenth century, had also been "restored" to their accustomed routines with the King's return, there to remain with but few changes until well on in the nineteenth century. The Clarendon Code of legislation in the sixteen-sixties, requiring strict adherence to the Prayer-book and the Thirty-nine Articles, had effectively closed the doors of universities and schools for some two hundred years, to all except those who would support the Established Church. Dissenters, or non-conformists as the Puritans then became, had to seek their education as well as their churches elsewhere.

The Act of Uniformity of 1662 applied not only to the professors and the candidates for degrees in the universities, but to every school-master, public or private, and to every tutor,—all were required to conform to the liturgy and to secure a license to teach. The Five-Mile Act levied a heavy fine against those who disobeyed, while at the same time it compelled the non-conformists to live away from the cities. Soon many small dissenting schools and academies developed, at first around some ejected teacher or professor, later around a group of tutors employed perhaps by a fund or by a group of ministers. Quite naturally, the ejected ministers and dissenting laymen would not send their sons to the universities, and often the ejected professors and tutors had been among the best teachers in their universities, the most progressive and efficient. As a result these schools flourished and gave such an excellent education that even the Anglicans sent their sons to them also, for they were open to all.

The dissenting academies, as distinct from the schools, were of university standing and were attended by students of 15, 16 and 17 years of age who would have gone to the universities had it not been for the Act of Uniformity. These academies soon became rivals of the universities who bitterly opposed them. In the first half of the eighteenth century there were thirty-four of them scattered through the land; but the most influential one of all, Warrington Academy, was not established till 1757. The lectures were given in English, though the study of the classics was still important. English books like Bacon's were read as literature. The curriculum was not directed solely to preparation for the ministry or the other professions, but included a general education and preparation for "commerce." This meant the study of "modern" subjects such as history, geography, science and French. Lectures were not formal, pedantic affairs but often conversations instead, and considerable help was given to individual students. Also, in great contrast to the universities, expenses were very low.

Warrington Academy, where Joseph Priestley taught from 1761-67, during its twenty-five years trained a total of nearly four hundred students in an atmosphere of free discussion, open-mindedness to new truth and recognition of the inalienable right of private judgment and of conscience. The dangers of growing Unitarianism and even of atheism led some of these academies toward the close of the century to emphasize credal matters for their students and gradually to decay, especially as debts added to their burdens. But in its heyday Warrington Academy was described as "the center of the liberal politics and the literary taste of the entire country." Manchester College at Oxford is its present-day descendant.

The academies with their firm but broad principles, their sober earnestness, their high moral tone and their independence of thought were in great contrast to the universities of the time. The academies advanced, while the universities sank to their lowest depths of attainment and discipline. An intellectual blight was upon them that was not lifted until the nineteenth century brought reform.

At the outset the universities had shared in the ferment over the new learning. Oxford had welcomed the Savilian professorships in astronomy and in geometry established there in 1619. Able men had held those posts, men like Henry Briggs and Christopher Wren who, themselves actively engaged in scientific pursuits, attracted about them others of similar interests. Thus in the Cromwellian period the Oxford Philosophical Society had grown out of the brilliant group connected with Wadham College when Wilkins was Warden, only to languish and die before the century closed. When Wilkins became Master of Trinity College, Cambridge, for a few months before the Restoration caused his ejection, he began the formation of a similar scientific group there, according to Dr. Birch some eighty years later. Whether this was true or not, science had flourished at Cambridge also. Newton was Lucasian professor of mathematics after 1669 for nearly a generation, overshadowing even such a distinguished scholar as Isaac Barrow who resigned that professorship to give place to the greater genius. Most of these men, like their associates in Gresham College, were among the early Fellows. Then times changed and academic activity died down. By the early eighteenth century the universities had reached a state of lethargy out of which they did not arise for scores of years. Their outlook was medieval, their training "formal, classical, Ciceronian, non-utilitarian." Reaction against Puritanism in church and state had included a reaction against changes in education which Puritanism had also supported.

It is not remarkable, therefore, that in the eighteenth century the non-conformist academies should flourish, nor that science at the same time should develop without instead of within the older institutions. It grew as individuals caught the spirit of such teaching as the academies represented, whether the individual scientists had their training in those academies or not. Thus in London the great Dr. John Hunter and his almost equally great brother William, built the science of medicine upon the foundations laid by Harvey and the other experimenters of the seventeenth century and at the same time they trained the younger men who came to them as pupils and assistants. Most notable of these latter was Edward Jenner who carried back to his country practice Hunter's admonition "Don't think, try," to discover the efficacy of vaccination against smallpox, the scourge of the century.

The influence of such teaching as Warrington and the other academies represented seems to have been a major stimulus to the scientific development that Great Britain was experiencing as the nineteenth century began. The Royal Society since its foundation had been the center of the scientific movement; but the leadership of the Society had grown slack. From these academies, not from the universities, came a fresh impetus to scientific work. It would be difficult to account for Britain's scientific growth without them.

Lord Macclesfield

What were the fortunes of the Royal Society after Sir Hans Sloane's retirement from the presidency in 1741? Six presidents in turn served the Society during the next three decades before Joseph Banks was elected in 1778. But until George III came to the throne in 1760 there was little notable scientific activity. The Society lacked the funds to undertake large enterprises and the government had its hands full with the War of the Austrian Succession and the Seven Years War.

Lord Macclesfield, for example, who was the second of the six presidents, helped in the computations necessary for the change over from the Old Style Julian calendar to the modern Gregorian one approved by Parliament in 1751. He realized the urgent need for new and better instruments at the Royal Observatory at Greenwich and, with satisfactory results, persuaded the Council to ask the government for funds to provide them. It was he, too, who recognized the importance of the proper editing of the *Philosophical Transactions,* under the goading of John Hill, and succeeded in establishing the Society's Committee of Papers, with full responsibility ever since. When discussions of the standard weights and measures in England and their comparison with French ones, brought out the need for greater accuracy in their definition, he had the Society order a standard brass yard of its own to be made,—a fact that was useful in 1834 when the government standard rods were destroyed in the burning of the parliament buildings.

Lightning Rods: Pointed or Knobbed

Of course, subjects in science as in other fields are more fashionable at one time than another, or appeal to popular interest more. One such subject during this mid-century was the outgrowth of Benjamin Franklin's experiments in 1727 with electricity. Not only did the practical value of his suggestion to use lightning rods to draw off electricity and protect buildings, appeal to the popular imagination; but also the presence in England of this notable American printer, author, statesman and scientist attracted attention to his person and to his ideas. The Royal Society had awarded him in 1753 its Copley Medal "on account of his curious experiments and observations on electricity" and as "deserving well of the philosophical world and of this learned body in particular." Two years later they elected him a Fellow, waiving his fees. In 1756 he signed the obligation and thereafter was often at the meetings and indeed served on the Council four different years.

The discussions over Franklin's lightning rods are of particular interest for they show how the Royal Society works through its committees or through individual Fellows without itself as a Society taking a stand on a particular theory or claim. They also show how political affairs can become intertwined with scientific ones. These discussions, in addition to the experiments used and the principles concerned, involved a theory that lightning rods would serve to attract lightning and to increase rather than to lessen the danger. Some argued that knobbed rods were preferable to the sharply pointed ones which Franklin advocated. Meantime their use gradually spread.

In 1769 the authorities in charge of St. Paul's Cathedral inquired of the Society about the best means of protecting that building, for another church had recently been struck by lightning and badly damaged. A committee of the Society, appointed by the Council and including Franklin, made a recommendation that there should be complete metallic communication between the cross at St. Paul's summit and the great lead-roofed dome, with the water-pipes used as conductors to the ground. This was done.

Three years later, the government, disturbed by the news of the destruction by lightning of some Italian powder magazines, sought ways of protecting its own storehouses of explosives. Again the Society was asked for its opinion and a committee was appointed which again included Franklin in its membership. Four of this committee recommended the use of pointed lightning rods, but the fifth strongly protested that pointed ones were likely to increase the quantity of electrical discharge, if not actually to occasion it. He recommended blunted conductors as safer because they would neither increase nor invite the electricity. The disagreement brought forth renewed discussion, and many papers on both sides of the question appeared in the *Philosophical Transactions*. Franklin wrote to a friend, "Here are some electricians that recommend knobs instead of points on the upper ends of the rods, from a supposition that points invite the stroke. It is true that points draw electricity at greater distances in the gradual silent way; but knobs will draw at the greatest distance a stroke."

The government adopted the pointed rods as recommended by the committee; but unfortunately in 1777 some magazines were struck and slightly injured and at the same time a house that was protected by the rods was also struck. Again the government asked the Society for an opinion and again the committee selected, a completely new one, reported in favor of pointed conductors. Thereupon the dissenting member of the other committee drew up a long report of his own experiments and sent it in protest to the government. They in turn referred it to the Society. A committee having tested these experiments and the conclusions drawn, reported against them. The dissenting member then wrote the government that the Society as a whole did not agree with its various committees. The government at once asked for sanction from the Society covering the previous committee reports. The answer finally sent by the secretary stated "that the Society has never since its first institution given an opinion as a body at large, but constantly by Committees. And that in the particular instance of the questions lately proposed by the Board of Ordnance, the Society has no reason to be dissatisfied with the report of its Committee."

In 1777 and 1778 when this matter was being thrashed out, the American Revolution was already in progress and Franklin was in Paris. Since he was an American, those who supported pointed rods soon became identified with the Americans and were considered disaffected subjects. People took up the quarrel without considering or caring about the scientific questions involved. Even King George himself, so it is stated, for political reasons had the lightning rods on his palace changed from pointed to blunt ones, and asked the president of the Royal Society to change its resolutions supporting points. Sir John Pringle replied, "Sire, I cannot reverse the laws and operations of nature." Whether or not the King then suggested that he had better resign, Sir John gave up the presidency that November, to be succeeded in the office by Joseph Banks.

Franklin refused to take any share in the controversy on the ground that he had said all that was necessary in a paper to the first committee which had been published. He did not wish to defend his scientific opinions but preferred to let them take their chance. If they were right, truth and experience would support them; if wrong they ought to be refuted and rejected. "The King's changing his pointed conductors for blunt ones is, therefore, a matter of small importance to me. If I had a wish about it, it would be, that he had rejected them altogether as ineffectual. For it is only since he thought himself and family safe from the thunder of Heaven, that he dared to use his own thunder in destroying his innocent subjects." Weld quotes a contemporary jingle:

"While you, great George, for knowledge hunt,
    And sharp conductors change for blunt,
        The nation's out of joint:
    Franklin a wiser course pursues,
    And all your thunder useless views,
        By keeping to the point."

Exploration

Politics and science make strange bedfellows indeed. George III, however, apparently did not let this matter of lightning rods blunt his already evident interest in scientific undertakings, nor turn him away from the activities of the Royal Society. In the very first year of his reign the government had actively supported a scientific expedition proposed by the Royal Society. Halley in 1714 had pointed out in *Philosophical Transactions* that the planet Venus would make a transit across the sun in 1761 and had urged that adequate preparation be made for observation of this rare phenomenon. The Council accordingly asked successfully for a government grant, since the funds of the Society were totally inadequate to care for the expense of the necessary expeditions. For the two authorized, the Council held many meetings to select observers, draft instructions and provide instruments. But the weather was bad at the island of St. Helena, and the other expedition for various reasons could not reach Bencoolen in Sumatra in time, so it stopped at the Cape of Good Hope in South Africa. Both groups did secure valuable astronomical data. As Venus was to make another transit in 1769 and not again for a century, the Council asked the government for further help including a much larger grant and transport at sea as well. Observers were to go to the Pacific, to Hudson Bay and to Madras.

Whereupon a young and wealthy Fellow secured permission to go along at his own expense on the expedition to the Pacific. Thus Joseph Banks with a group of assistants accompanied Lieutenant Cook on the expedition of the Endeavour during the years 1768 to 1771. Not only did they observe the transit of Venus but they also explored the coasts of Australia and learned much about it and the islands nearby. This experience in exploration was not his first, for Banks had already been to the coasts of Newfoundland and Labrador on a navy ship with an officer friend of his.

Immediately after the return of the Endeavour, Cook, now a Captain, made ready for an exploration to the Antarctic. Again the Council was busy with instructions and preparations, and Banks again asked to go along. This time his party was too large to be accommodated on the Admiralty ships, so permission was refused him.

Instead, he chartered a ship and went to Iceland. This summer's expedition had a curious sequel many years later. Banks had brought back many Icelandic books and manuscripts as well as specimens, and thereafter had been much interested in the fortunes of the island. During the Napoleonic war when England seized the Danish fleet, the Icelanders were cut off from their usual food supplies and were suffering great hardship. No Danish ship could get through the blockade to bring them supplies. It was through Sir Joseph Banks, one of its members, that the Board of Trade in 1808 was persuaded to grant licenses for protection from the British fleet to the Danish ships carrying relief to the island.[1]

Not content with the expeditions it had fostered to the South Seas and the Antarctic, the Council of the Royal Society turned to the Arctic regions, recommending an exploration which the government undertook in 1773 with its guidance and advice.

These were the years between the end of the Seven Years War and the outbreak of the American Revolution. England had become mistress of the seas and ruler over vast realms that now lay open for development. Of course, the government could now readily join with the science-lovers, if for different reasons, to explore the oceans and to uncover the resources of far distant lands. John Harrison's chronometers were proving their usefulness in solving the problem of longitude for the King's ships. Dr. James Lind's treatise on scurvy (1753), and Stephen Hales' studies on the application of science to hygiene, to the questions of pure water, air and food—these, too, would have direct bearing on the successful outcome of long voyages. Thus by their work as individuals and through their Council, the Fellows of the Royal Society had an active share in the growth of the colonial empire.

Exploration slowed down, however, if it did not entirely

1 Weld, II, 109-111.

stop, while England was involved in wars at the close of the century,—the American and the French Revolutions and the Napoleonic Wars. Later, after the Congress of Vienna, the Royal Society through its Council again urged support by the government for further exploration, this time of the practicability of a North-West Passage north of Greenland. The expedition did secure scientific information of value, even if it did not find such a passage. The Council also supported plans for a North Polar expedition. And ever since, the Royal Society has continued to further exploration.

Not long before the outbreak of the French Revolution the Society requested a government grant to carry out a triangulation from Greenwich to the French coast where it would connect with the French triangulation and so help to determine the difference in longitude between the Paris observatory and the English one at Greenwich. The theodolite made for this purpose in 1784 was also used in 1821 when the observations were re-checked at the request of the *Académie des Sciences*. Later the instrument on loan from the Society was used by the government in its ordnance survey.

George III and Science

In much of this work, in contrast to the common American view of his stodginess, George III took an active interest and on occasion supported the Council's recommendations and requests to the government. Immediately after his accession in 1760 he had studied experimental philosophy for a time, especially liking mechanical and agricultural science, so much so that a name for him then was "Farmer George." He personally supported Harrison and his chronometers when there was a dispute between him and the Board of Longitude over the chronometric method of determining longitude in preference to stellar observation. When William Herschel discovered the planet Uranus, winning the Copley Medal and a Fellowship thereby, the astronomer wanted the planet named Georgium Sidus, both to date the time and place of its discovery and to do honor to "the best of kings, who is a liberal protector of every art and science" and of the discoverer himself. Herschel was welcomed at court that year (1781) to exhibit the skies to the royal family through his telescopes and, through Banks' intervention, was privately appointed court astronomer with £200 a year. The King ordered Herschel to make telescopes for him which he then gave away, he assisted Herschel in his remarkable observations by large grants of funds, and even went himself to inspect the great telescope Herschel constructed.

During these same years it was the King's interest and personal support that backed the government's offer to house the Royal Society in rooms rent free. He created its president, Banks, a baronet, and Banks in turn became his unofficial adviser on science, being especially useful in directing the collectors who were sent abroad in the interest of the royal gardens at Kew. The last years of George's long life were shadowed by much illness. His son as Prince Regent seemingly took less interest in science, though as George IV he too became a Patron of the Society.

Crane Court to Somerset House

After his return from Iceland, Banks had settled down in London there to become a patron and promoter of scientific activity—"a dilettante" of science—for the rest of his long life. Elected a Fellow in 1766, twelve years later Banks became president. Immediately, like Newton long before him, he was confronted by the problem of housing for the Society.

Two years earlier the government had offered to provide rooms in Somerset House, rent free, for the Royal Society as well as the Antiquarian Society. Somerset House had been the residence of Queen Charlotte, but other pro-

PLATE 14. Sir Isaac Newton, President of the Royal Society, 1703-1727

(From *The Record of the Royal Society*, London, 1940, by courtesy of the Royal Society)

PLATE 16. The Meeting-Room of the Royal Society at Somerset House 1780-18

vision was being made for her and her former home was being torn down so that a new building could be built "for the service of the public." At first the Council did not consider adequate the provision suggested there for the Society. But Crane Court was now too small for the greatly increased membership. The new rooms would be convenient to the other society, they were in a good location and there would be no rent. Consequently, the Council made the move in 1780 and sold the Crane Court property two years later. As the new space provided was somewhat limited, it was at this time, in preparation for the move, that the Council decided to offer the Society's collections—the development of the original "repository" of the early days—to the British Museum to be added to the collections of Sir Hans Sloane already there. This was "the considerable donation" for which the trustees expressed their gratitude in 1781.

One wonders if the curious item that the Council in 1798 gave £500 "as a voluntary contribution towards the defense of the country at this critical period"[2] of Napoleon's rise to power and the success of his armies under the Directory was linked not only with patriotism but also with a sense of obligation to the government for the Society's freedom from the expense of housing. At any rate the item reflects a vastly improved condition of the treasury as compared with the situation Secretary Hans Sloane undertook to remedy a century before.

Sir Joseph Banks

The presidency of Sir Joseph Banks extended from 1778 until his death in 1820, but during the last dozen years of this time he was in poor health. Gout in particular deprived him of the use of his legs; that did not hinder him from being taken in his wheelchair to the various meetings with his accustomed regularity, or from being wheeled

2 Weld, II, 226.

about among his guests. One who saw him in those days recorded an impression of massive eye-brows and of an imposing appearance made all the more impressive by his silence with foreign guests. "Speaking no other language than English, and carrying scientific knowledge little beyond the domain of natural science, he nevertheless looked the governing power of the Royal Society and was such in reality." [3] Just before his death he offered to resign but the Council asked him to remain.

In public life Sir Joseph had an exceptional position through his wealth, his independence of parliamentary and public disputes, and his wide background of foreign exploration. As president of the Society he was also chairman of the Board of Longitude, and of the Board of Visitors for the Royal Observatory, and he was ex officio a trustee of the British Museum. Often consulted by the government, he exercised his influence literally far and wide,—from his support of the African Society to his directions concerning the collections in Kew Gardens. Because of his own primary interest in botany, horticulture, agriculture and the raising of live-stock, he probably was not as appreciative of the workers in mathematics and the physical sciences. But it is now thought that he did not discriminate against them as "Peter Pindar," for instance, had charged early in his administration. It is true, however, that when he first became president he had expressed the intention of scrutinizing closely the certificates in support of candidates in order to ensure adequately qualified Fellows; but he had let his good intentions go unfulfilled.

One historian of the Society interprets Sir Joseph's failure to strengthen the scientific aspects of the Society as caused by his feeling that the Royal Society was a trust committed to his care, rather than a living institution to be used for the promotion of natural knowledge in every way possible. Stagnation was the result.

[3] Sir Henry Holland, cited in Geikie, *Annals of the Royal Society Club* (London, 1917) 237.

11

EXPANSION VERSUS TRADITION

D URING Newton's and Sloane's presidencies until
well into the eighteenth century, the Royal Society had kept in the forefront of scientific progress despite its difficulties. Under less distinguished presidents in the mid-century it had done useful work. But by
the latter part of the eighteenth century and in the early
nineteenth, the Society seemed to mark time while science
progressed more or less independently of its leadership.
London was no longer the sole center of wealth and of
intellectual activity; the new cities of the north and west
like Manchester, Leeds and Birmingham, were gaining in
importance as the industrial revolution gathered strength.
From them now came new ideas, new wealth and new
vigor. The slow-moving, comfortable old Society under
Sir Joseph Banks had so failed to recognize the widening
spread and the gathering force of this scientific growth
that by 1830 a critic complained that "science was without a
head."

Science Outside the Universities

The dissenting academies were strong outside London and some of the best of them, such as Warrington Academy, were at the height of their influence in the latter part of the eighteenth century as centers of culture for their immediate regions. Joseph Priestley, the Unitarian minister teaching "languages and belles lettres" at Warrington was working away at his own chemical experiments which resulted in the discovery of oxygen. Professors from these academies and other enthusiasts began offering to the general public lectures in series or singly on "Natural Philosophy." Many books on that subject were published in English during the century. Popular interest in science was on the alert.

Men interested in science formed themselves into clubs for reading and discussion. Perhaps the most famous was the Lunar Society of Birmingham, founded in 1766 by Charles Darwin's grandfather, Dr. Erasmus Darwin. It met monthly on the Monday night nearest the full moon; hence its name. Among its members were Priestley, Herschel the musician-astronomer, and Watt of steam-engine fame.

In the meantime the old universities continued on their way, largely indifferent to any except classical studies. Cambridge University recognized mathematics as a major subject when it established the Mathematical Tripos in 1747, but not for a hundred years more did it recognize Natural Science in a similar fashion. The mere fact that a university had a professor of chemistry or of experimental philosophy during this period did not necessarily mean that the professor was a specialist. Richard Watson, professor of chemistry at Cambridge, according to Miss Turner, related that at the time of his appointment he knew nothing of the subject; but by experimenting for several hours daily in his laboratory he was soon able to lecture to large and distinguished audiences. He was at the same time Regius professor of divinity, a bishop, and rector of several parishes!

Anyone interested in scientific study had better set up his own workshop or "physical cabinet" and struggle along with his own problems. Certainly the universities had no conception of serving as centers of research for many years to come. Natural science and the study of botany in particular could be undertaken by individuals without too elaborate equipment. This may in part explain the great interest in natural specimens and their study which followed the pioneer studies of John Ray at the end of the preceding century. The formation of collections like that of Sir Hans Sloane aroused interest, as did the work of those naturalists whom Addison, Steele and John Hill gleefully caricatured. Even John Hill's own books, one should remember, were said to have been a powerful influence in spreading a wider interest in botany.

Popular attention was also aroused by the experiments in electricity which Benjamin Franklin's presence in England helped to dramatize. More and more, interest in scientific subjects was spreading from the "gentlemen of noble bloud" of Sprat's day to the middle classes,—the country doctors like Jenner, the German music-teacher, Herschel, who became one of the world's foremost astronomers, and the apothecary's apprentice from Cornwall, known later as Sir Humphry Davy, president of the Royal Society.

The Mechanics Institutes

Education for the poor was restricted mainly to the three R's. But Adam Smith spoke for a number of thoughtful people in his day when in *The Wealth of Nations* he advocated education as a way of offsetting the deadening monotony of routine machine work and of the division of labor. Sometimes the workers themselves who helped individual scientists to make their laboratory equipment showed such intelligent interest in scientific knowledge that they too were invited to hear the lectures.

The leader in setting up a systematic education for the workers was John Anderson, professor of natural philosophy at Glasgow. As early as 1760 he held evening classes for them. George Birkbeck, professor of physics on the fund left by Anderson in his will, welcomed to his classes the artisans who helped him build his equipment. Soon he had to organize separate lectures for them in another building. This became known as Anderson's Institution. It was the forerunner of the Mechanics Institutes that played an important part in the education of the workingmen before public funds were made available for this purpose following the extension of the franchise in the middle of the nineteenth century.

These Institutes were formed in the towns by the men themselves. The Society of Arts founded in 1754 helped also, for its aims were to encourage the practical applications of science by books, by exhibits of specimens, and finally in the next century by its system of examinations. Similarly the Society for the Diffusion of Useful Knowledge, established in 1827, issued penny booklets written by some of the best authorities, so that a mechanic could have something brief but substantial to read in his leisure hours, at a price that he could afford. It is hard to realize now that public libraries were not founded until the middle of the nineteenth century.

The Mechanics Institutes in various towns drew together in groups and pooled their resources, exchanging lecturers as well as books. By 1850 there were more than 600 of these organizations and over 100,000 members. As a result, scientific knowledge was spreading far into sections of the population that before 1800 had had small access to it.

New Scientific Associations

While this interest in science was spreading among the workers, science enthusiasts among the more well-to-do also wanted to share their experiences and discuss their common interest. The formation of the specialized scientific societies was the result. The first of these was the Linnean Society, founded in 1778 with the blessing of Sir Joseph Banks, and appropriately enough, housed after his death for a time in his home in Soho Square. Upon the death of the great Swedish naturalist, Carl Linné, the founder of modern biological classification, his library and collections had been offered for purchase to Sir Joseph. He did not care to buy them, but a younger man, Dr. James Smith, at breakfast with Sir Joseph, learned of this opportunity and seized it for himself. Dr. Smith, helped by Sir Joseph, founded the Linnean Society and ultimately turned over to it the valuable treasures he had so unexpectedly purchased. The success of this new society was swift and was recognized in 1802 by a royal charter.

A few years later Count Rumford won Sir Joseph Banks' support for his own idea, the Royal Institution. This was organized at a meeting held in Sir Joseph's house and was established in 1799, not as a rival to the Royal Society in the promotion of natural knowledge, but as an aid to science through the diffusion of that knowledge and through the general introduction of useful mechanical inventions and improvements. It advocated by lectures and experiments the teaching of the application of science to the common purposes of life. Reflecting the contemporary interest in the working-man's concern with science, Count Rumford planned to have it serve as a training center for young men in mechanics. These students were to be boarded at the Institution for three or four months to secure "a perfect knowledge of new and useful inventions applicable to the common purposes of life."

Count Rumford himself gave lectures on heat and the

use of various fuels. Soon after Humphry Davy had joined the Institution to direct the laboratory and to lecture in chemistry, the Count returned to Munich and the work of the Institution was put on a different footing. The training of young mechanics was abandoned entirely. Research work was developed, while the public lectures became increasingly popular.

The Royal Institution and the Royal Society have been closely associated from the very beginning, and many of the Fellows were members of the other organization also. Davy made the chemistry lectures fashionable. Michael Faraday, his successor as director, carried out there his momentous researches in electricity that made possible the development of the whole vast electrical industry. At the same time he built up the popular Friday evening lectures and instituted the famous Christmas talks which enchanted the children for whom he gave them. His simple clarity and easy eloquence on science subjects have rarely been equalled. His example has been followed by other directors of the Institution, notably in recent times by Sir William Bragg, Nobel prize-winner for researches in physics, and a lucid speaker.

Even among scientists today, these two organizations, the Royal Institution and the Royal Society, are sometimes confused, while among laymen there is limited knowledge either of their separate histories or of their difference in purpose. In fact, the lay public is apt to know the Institution best as it throngs the amphitheater to hear a clear and often brilliant exposition of scientific work and to see demonstrations performed and slides shown. For the Royal Institution is a working center,—indeed, Weld said it had been called "the workshop of the Royal Society"—while the Royal Society is an association of scientists to further research by advice and criticism, by assignment of funds and award of medals, and by the recognition which election to its fellowship brings today to eminent scientists. One is an institute, the other a society.

Sir Joseph Banks as president of the Royal Society had

thrown his great influence into helping the Linnean Society and the Royal Institution get established. Then his attitude to separate scientific groups changed. As these developed, he was willing to welcome them if they would be subsidiary parts of the Royal Society, but he strongly opposed them as independent organizations. They, in turn, considered that the *Philosophical Transactions* did not have adequate space to publish all the research being done, nor did they consider that subordination to the Society would give them sufficient independence. In spite of Sir Joseph's opposition, the Geological Society formed its own organization in 1807, as did the Astronomical Society a dozen years or so later. Others also were rapidly established.

Sir Joseph particularly opposed the formation of the Astronomical Society, lest it rob the Royal Society of many of its ablest members. A close friend and admirer of his, Sir James Barrow, recorded that Sir Joseph had remarked to him: "I see plainly that all these new-fangled associations will finally dismantle the Royal Society, and not leave the old lady a rag to cover her." But, Sir James went on, no harm was done as people became members of both organizations.

In 1836, after listing twelve of the new organizations "and above all the British Association," Granville wrote of them as "shooting upwards into mighty trees, and interlacing their far spreading branches over the Royal Oak planted by Charles and reared by Newton, (once the sovereign and sole occupier of the soil, but now stunted and neglected,) to cast their blighting shadow over it, whereby it shall perish, entombed before its death." One indication of the seriousness of this new development, he pointed out, was that, since 1800, for thirty years the *Philosophical Transactions* had not published a single paper on botany, and very few on zoology, geology and astronomy. The Linnean Society was obviously absorbing the entire botanical branch of science, and the other new groups were threatening to do the same for their respective branches.

The Society's "Second Childhood"

Meanwhile, according to Granville, the Society slept "its slumbers of conscious and secure importance," unaware of the new organizations' "luxuriancy of numbers and structural organs, and power of production equaling almost Australian vegetation." To avert this doom and to help bring about wholesome reforms, Granville sought to describe "things as they are" in the Society since 1800 and to indicate the reforms needed.

What were the evils of the situation that made Dr. Granville anonymously charge in 1830 that science was without a head? And Charles Babbage, the skilled mathematician of calculating-machine fame, declare that same year that the Society was sinking into its second childhood, greatly regretted by its children, the separate scientific associations?

Sir Joseph Banks' Autocracy

Criticism concerning the Society had not ceased when John Hill died. Early in Sir Joseph Banks' administration, he had had to contend for his executive authority with the jealousies of other officers of the Society and their supporters. When it became apparent that one of these men was haughtily directing a personal attack on the president, hoping to succeed him in the presidency himself, the Society, antagonized by the tone of the speeches, strongly upheld Sir Joseph. Thus firmly established, Sir Joseph's long tenure in office, combined with his powerful personality, made the position one of such autocratic power that after his death the Society struggled for years before the abuses that arose were checked. Meantime Sir Joseph's opponents had recourse to printed publication of their grievances against him and the Society.

The quarrel arose in 1782 over the treatment accorded

by the president and the Council to Dr. Hutton, the assistant to the secretaries in charge of foreign correspondence. This was a position created early in the eighteenth century to lighten the load of work upon the two secretaries. It carried with it an honorarium of twenty pounds. The duties involved writing such letters to foreigners as the president and Council might direct; but as the assistant himself, though a Fellow, was not necessarily a Councilor he sometimes had to carry out instructions without having heard the matter discussed. Trouble often developed. The situation was not finally remedied until the next century, when the position of third secretary in charge of foreign correspondence was established to rank with the other secretaries.

Dr. Hutton was a distinguished mathematician living at Woolwich, some distance from London. The Council voted that the foreign secretary should reside in London. Dr. Hutton a month or so later resigned. His friends among the Fellows decided that he had been ill-treated, and, indeed, perhaps the matter had been handled rather summarily. The details are unimportant at this distance. What developed out of the series of meetings which the Society held that winter to discuss his case was the vote of confidence in the president. As a result, not only was Sir Joseph more firmly established in his own position, but also his influence over the secretaries was strengthened. One of them, a supporter of Dr. Hutton, was forced to resign two years later.

This resignation came about in connection with the publication of an anonymous pamphlet, *An Authentic Narrative of the Dissensions and Debates in the Royal Society* (1784) which was quite evidently the work of Dr. Hutton's supporters. When Mr. Maty, still secretary, offered the pamphlet to the Society as a gift, Sir Joseph refused to present the customary motion of thanks, saying that he considered the work an insult to the Society for it was full of misrepresentations. It was after this meeting that Mr. Maty resigned. Sir Joseph then specifically asked the Society to elect as secretary a man whom he favored, as over against the candidate proposed by the dissidents. Again Sir Joseph was overwhelmingly supported by the election, and from then on his control over the Society and the administration remained unshaken.

The anonymous pamphlet today makes interesting reading, more because of its tone than because of the long speeches it contains. One gets an impression of the Society's meetings on Dr. Hutton's case as having been the discussions of a club of notable men in London society, expressing their disapproval of statements made not only by cries of "Order," and "shame," but by "the clattering of sticks" on the floor. (Can one not picture the gold-headed canes of the gouty old gentlemen?) References in the speeches to the black-balling—rejection—of candidates by the Council supposedly at the president's request made to several of the secretaries and Councilors, brought even stronger protests, "with accompaniment of sticks." The opposition, debarred from airing their grievances in detail at these meetings, printed much of what they had intended to say in this pamphlet and promised more later.

This unfulfilled promise is worth quoting:

Shortly will be published,
A History of certain Exclusions from the Royal Society. In which it is shewn, that neither Mathematicians, nor Country Physicians, nor London Physicians, nor Army Agents, nor Practical Astronomers, nor Authors, nor Scholars by Profession of any description, are proper persons to be made Fellows of the Royal Society of London, instituted for the Promotion of Natural Knowledge.

As the result of that winter of many meetings over Dr. Hutton's case, and in spite of the publication of this *Authentic Account*, Sir Joseph found himself in supreme control of the Society, to direct its affairs for more than a generation as he thought fit. The anonymous pamphlet admitted that the victory of the majority had been received by the president's friends in a moderate and humble manner, not as conquerors, and that the president was said to have borne no resentment against those who had been most active in impeaching his conduct. He would try to be more cautious in the future, it reported, seeking yet more information about the candidates and stating that in future his Council would be not "a meer list of honorable names" as formerly, but "a Committee of Men of Letters," that "his deportment to the officers of the Society would be more liberal, and his treatment of the servants more mild and just." (One must not forget that Sir Joseph had been an explorer and a seafarer for years before he settled down in London and that such experiences probably did not lessen any tendencies to exercise a somewhat autocratic authority.)

Criticism continued. One of the more vocal of these critics, a military surgeon and a satirical poet, John Wolcot, under the pseudonym of "Peter Pindar" published *Peter's Prophecy, or the President and Poet; or, An Important Epistle to Sir Joseph Banks, on the Approaching Election of a President of the Royal Society* (1789). In this dialogue the Poet warns Sir Joseph by name to beware St. Andrews' Day for "Think what a host of enemies you make!" Sir Joseph's hospitality—his house "a tavern in Soho"—his friendship with the King, his dominance over the elections to the Society, his own lack of scientific output,—all these and more are targets for the satirist's verses. He makes Sir Joseph say:

> "I've star-gazers enough;
> I now look round for different kind of stuff:
> Besides—*untitled* members are mere swine;
> I wish for *princes* on my list to shine;
> I'll have a company of stars and strings;
> I'll have a proud society of *kings*! . . .
>
> Yes, yes, my friend, my tea and butter'd rolls
> Have found an easy pass to people's souls:
> My well-tim'd dinners (*certain folks* revere)
> Have left this easy bosom nought to fear.

The turnpike road to people's hearts, I find,
Lies through their guts, or I mistake mankind;
Besides, while thus I boast my Sov'reign's smile,
Let raggamuffins rage, and rogues revile."

"Peter" mockingly warns him:

"With solemn, sentimental step, so slow,
I see you through the streets of London go,
With poring, studious, staring, earth-nail'd eye,
As heedless of the mob that bustles by;
This *was* a scheme of wisdom, let me say,
But lo, this trap for fame hath had its day;
And let me tell you, what I've urg'd before,
The restless Members look for something more."

Even Sir Humphry Davy, according to Barrow who was Sir Joseph's friend, considered Sir Joseph "a courtier at heart" who "made his house a circle too like a court." He held that Sir Joseph had "not much reading, and no profound information" and required that he be regarded as patron. Also, he readily sanctioned "gross flattery." Barrow, on the other hand, held Sir Joseph as the standard by which other presidents should be judged—and most of his successors (by 1849) would be found wanting!

The Society's "Dotage"

The restless members, however, had to wait for a good many years before Sir Joseph ceased to control the Society. As a consequence the eighteenth century Society was carried over for some twenty years into the nineteenth. Laxity marked its administration and stagnation its affairs as Sir Joseph's ill-health and old age increased in a period of change in the world of politics and of science. Ten years or so after Sir Joseph's death, Granville, Babbage and the other reformers of the eighteen-thirties feared that the Society had fallen into its dotage perhaps never to recover. Babbage went further than Granville, declaring that science itself in England was declining seriously, partly through its neglect by the universities and partly by that system of education which means that "scientific knowledge today scarcely exists among the higher classes," as discussions in parliament showed. Not only had the Royal Society, he charged, failed to arouse the higher classes and the universities, but it had also opposed the formation of the scientific associations and failed to use election to membership as a stimulus to distinctive achievement in the field of science. Thereupon he devoted the remaining three-quarters of his book to the misrule in the Society.

Both critics were Fellows, one a physician, the other a mathematician and inventor, and both were writing from knowledge gained since their respective elections in 1817 and in 1816. Granville backed up his assertions with more facts and figures, for his history was a re-issue, revised and amplified, of his *Science Without a Head* published in the heat of the campaign of 1830 for the Society's president. Babbage's book was also part of that campaign, a forthright, vigorous presentation of a too gloomy view of British science. As an appendix he reprinted without comment a report on a German association of scientists that had held annual week-long conferences for a number of years past. The formation that next year (1831) of the British Association for the Advancement of Science holding similar conferences is attributed largely to the influence of Babbage's book. (Seventeen years later, the American Association for the Advancement of Science was established at the suggestion of the Association of American Geologists and Naturalists.)

The picture of the Royal Society which both men presented has many elements in common. Granville described it as "a mere club-like association of highly respectable, well educated and very honorable men, with every kind and no kind of scientific knowledge." To black-ball, or reject, a candidate for membership was therefore to impart a stigma on the individual, mortifying to bear, and having no reference to his scientific abilities. It might be due to "private feelings, professional jealousies and political rancor." Of the four men recently black-balled, one was a physician and notable obstetrician, Granville claimed, whose "religious tenets were supposed to be at variance with those of high churchmen."

Babbage wrote of a candidate: "If he has the good fortune to be perfectly unknown by any literary or scientific achievement, however small, he is quite sure of being elected as a matter of course. If he has unfortunately written on any subject concerned with science, or is supposed to be acquainted with any branch of it, members begin to inquire what he has done to deserve the honour; and unless he has powerful friends, he has a fair chance of being black-balled." In addition, membership in the Society was a distinction "which has become insignificant from its unlimited extension."

By the Charters, control of the Society's affairs was vested in the president and the Council. The Council had twenty-one members, from among whom the officers were selected. But Granville charged that the Society was in the hands of a Venetian oligarchy, being ruled by a doge and a Council of Ten, for that was the usual attendance at Council meetings, and two-thirds of the Council's membership were well-known favorites of the president. The Society elected ten members to the Council each year, but those "purged" and those elected in their places were really the nominees of the president, since the Council prepared the voting lists for the Fellows. And Babbage claimed that the Council in its turn voted for whomever the president named from a slip of paper in his pocket, without previous notification or discussion.

Some men had been councilors for years at a time, and all too few of them were scientists. Those scientists who were elected found the meetings concerned with trifles, the business handled mere routine, and their suggestions disregarded. They soon gave up in disgust, or even refused to serve. In consequence, "the president's clique or camarilla," a small minority of the Council, controlled the Society. As Granville looked at the situation, "jobbing—

personal interest—patronage—political sympathy and antipathy—nepotism—jesuitism and favoritism—" these have always exerted their baneful interest and always will, despite Babbage's idealistic hopes to the contrary.

The president's powers in recent years had greatly increased through the power of patronage. The award of medals and of lectureships in the control of the Council, the appointment of salaried officers and assistants and of delegates or representatives, the assignment of printing to be done and of hospitality to be rendered all involved money. Babbage charged that Sir Humphry's successor in office had "grasped at despotic power." But neither he nor Granville upheld the charges made by another Fellow, Sir James South, whom Granville quotes as alleging malfeasance, though they did bring evidence of great laxity.

Proposals for Reform

Granville did not agree with Babbage that the Copley, Rumford and Royal Medals had been unwisely allotted, except possibly in the one case of Dr. Wollaston who had kept secret his method of making platinum malleable, and so grown rich while hindering the further advance of scientific discovery. But they both made it apparent that the lectureships in some cases seemed to turn into small annuities to some worthy person, instead of being used for the furtherance of science.

The Fairchild lectureship had been held for 26 years by one clergyman. Was that annual sermon actually preached? Who heard it and where was it given? Why should it not be made a public occasion of importance that would promote science and each year give recognition for distinguished achievement? Similarly, the three pounds of the Croonian lectureship had gone to Sir Edward Home as a kind of annual pension for twenty years, although Sir Edward would have kept on with his distinguished medical researches without that award.

A Finance committee was much needed to oversee expenditures and to put down abuses. Most of all the Fellows needed to know more about the yearly accounts of the Society than what the treasurer told them in the annual statement which presented only total receipts and total expenditures. An active Finance committee could perhaps limit the costs of printing, for were there not too many copies of the president's annual address made, and were not the expensively printed annual reports to the Society from the Royal Astronomer later sold in bulk as waste paper by the printer? Reforms suggested by an individual councilor met with no success for they were apt to interfere with somebody's perquisite, like the waiter's commission on each bottle of wine used as refreshments, or the porter's tip from each Fellow to whose home he delivered the voting lists. Therefore the Council had refused to have the lists distributed at a meeting previous to the election.

Full publicity about these and other weaknesses could result in restoration of vitality to the Society, but the crucial difficulty still remained. How could distinction be restored to election to membership? The two critics disagreed on how this should be brought about. Babbage wanted the elections held down till the Society numbered 400 instead of over 600. Granville thought such a limitation "ludicrous." He wanted to achieve the goal of a distinguished membership by an elaborate system of voting to fill vacancies as they arose in the classes of membership he would have established.

In addition, Babbage held that the president should not hold office for more than two years, to avoid the dominating effect of a powerful personality imposed on an organization over a period of years. Obviously he had not forgotten Sir Joseph's power. Granville was more reserved, for he was writing when a Royal Prince was president.

The Council of course should be more responsive to the Fellows and less concerned with their own well-being. Were there not several instances of too many offices, each with an honorarium, held by one man, and that man a Councilor? It seems significant in this connection that when the Donation Fund was set up shortly before this dissension broke out, its founder who had been president for the few months between Sir Joseph's death and the next election, specifically declared the members of the Council ineligible for the benefits of the Fund.

Granville agreed with Babbage that reforms within the Society were long overdue, but he did not agree that the Society was dying nor that science in England had passed its heyday with Newton's death. Brilliant men like Dalton who created the table of atomic weights, Sir Humphry Davy, inventor of the miner's safety lamp and noted chemist, young Michael Faraday, Dr. Jenner, the father of vaccination against smallpox,—these and many more were doing fine work. But neither of these two critics shows any awareness of the rising interest in and knowledge of science that the Mechanics Institutes were fostering among the workers. They were discussing science as it was in the hands of the aristocracy. Social standing was an important factor in their thinking for it affected membership as well as office-holding in the Society.

The Society's Situation

To the reader it is apparent that the club-like organization of the eighteenth century was still being maintained. But science was not at fault, nor was it declining. The Society was not due to die, though it seemed to be in its dotage. It simply had failed to keep pace with changing times and conditions. Once the encrustations of petty privilege, of administrative laxity and official indifference were swept away and the membership situation clarified, the Society showed that far from being in its second childhood, it only then began to attain its full strength.

As a further comment on the Society's situation at this time, one catches significant contemporary overtones in the preamble to the rules of the British Association,—that lusty rival whose rapid growth so alarmed Granville when he saw 2000 assembled in Dublin in 1835 at its annual conference. Its purposes were "to give a stronger impulse and a more systematic direction of scientific enquiry; to promote the intercourse of those who cultivate science in different parts of the British Empire with one another and with foreign philosophers; to obtain a more general attention to the objects of science and a removal of any disadvantages of a public kind which impede its progress."

Entrenched weaknesses are hard to remove or to offset. The Society had to pass through a difficult period of reform, reaction and reform, accompanied by much dissension. But the liberal temper of the mid-nineteenth century strengthened the reformers of the Society as well as the reformers of parliament and of affairs in England outside the Society. The widening spread of scientific knowledge among the people, combined with the forces of wealth and invention released by the industrial revolution, had its effect also. Between 1820 and 1850 the changes needed were made.

12

UNHAPPY YEARS

As THE SEVENTEENTH CENTURY saw the birth of modern science in England, the nineteenth saw science develop into many branches. While Boyle had formerly complained about the scarcity of scientists, now their number was swelling rapidly. The causes for this notable expansion were many. Genius itself is latent in every generation. The industrial revolution provided the means for scientific study and the wealth necessary to promote it. The scientists had available or were developing a variety of tools of increased precision from microscopes to slide-rules. They were using the experimental method ever more rigorously. They were overthrowing ancient and mistaken theories by fruitful hypotheses supported by discoveries that were startling at times. Their cooperative activities in associations and societies led to increased publication of scientific books as well as of journals. British science as a result made great strides in the nineteenth and twentieth centuries.

"An Unhappy Period"

In the science of the seventeenth century the Royal Society, as we have seen, played a leading part, and a not unimportant rôle in the eighteenth. At the beginning of the nineteenth it was no longer a leader. In Sir William Bragg's phrase, this was an "unhappy period" when internal dissensions, the unchecked growth in membership and the formation of independent societies to take over special sections of the Society's work, brought about denunciations of the Society's management and laments over the contemporary decline of science. Yet public interest and study were growing apace. What was needed in the Royal Society was to have the leadership and the control over its affairs shifted from the hands of the antiquarians, statesmen, lawyers and patrons of science into the hands of men of science themselves. Amateurs must give way to scientists. Then the scientists could adapt the old Society to the new age and shift it from dependence on its past laurels to active participation in the work of the present and the future.

There were three major stages in this transformation as it was finally worked out. First, the scientists themselves had to achieve the election of a scientist as president and secure a majority of places on the Council for themselves. Next, they had to learn the facts about the Society's administration, particularly its finances, in order to clear away abuses. Lastly, they had to confine the membership to genuine scientists and by limiting the number of Fellows elected each year, make election to membership a high privilege.

These readjustments were not made in a day. Nearly thirty years elapsed before all the necessary measures were taken, and still more years before the reforms could effect the transformation of an eighteenth-century, club-like assembly of notables into a scientific association with importance, power and prestige in the twentieth century.

Shifts in administrative procedure may not be dramatic in themselves, but their consequences sometimes have dramatic results.

An account of these changes involves a certain amount of reference to the scientific movements of the day, but this can only be incidental. The history of scientific progress, especially after 1800, belongs in the hands of the specialists, for as the sciences became highly technical, they developed their own vocabularies. Before this period a layman could make shift to comprehend the language of science; from now on the new ideas involved new terms and new phrases that require a training in the science itself to be intelligible. One has only to compare the experiments reported by Dr. Wilkins in 1661 with those described in any scientific journal today to appreciate this difference. There is room, besides, for a thorough going study of the scientific work of the Society, especially during the hundred years since its reorganization, a study that will also trace the effects of its activities and its influence upon governmental and imperial policies at home and abroad. A writer who is both historian and scientist would be best qualified to handle so complex and highly specialized a subject in all its ramifications. What some of these ramifications are can only be suggested in these chapters.

The Age of Reform

The reorganization in the Royal Society needs to be considered against the background of other movements in the history of this period; for they were closely interwoven. As we have noted before, the year in which Sir Joseph Banks died saw also the death of his royal friend, George III, after years of ill-health. The Prince Regent, now George IV, though interested in the Society, was not so marked a friend of science as his father had been; but he too signed the Charter-book to become Royal Patron, and he began the award of the Royal Medals.

By 1820 the Napoleonic Wars had been over for five years or so, and Napoleon was an exile on St. Helena. On the continent the spirit of the French Revolution upheld the forces of liberalism and reform in many fields as they struggled against the reactionary opposition typified by Metternich whose name marks this age. The uprisings of 1820, unsuccessful in general, were but the forerunners of yet more serious upheavals to come and ultimately of the revolutions of 1848 which toppled Metternich out of power and changed the map of Europe. The Austrian's downfall brought hope to the liberals everywhere only to have that hope temporarily stifled by the return to power of the reactionary forces seemingly as stable as ever.

England was spared the actual bloodshed which accompanied these events in many European countries. But she too had her struggles between the reactionaries and the liberals. Chief among the Tories was the old Duke of Wellington, hero of the Napoleonic days. Among the liberals were men fired by the ideals of the revolutionaries who had created the United States and had attacked autocracy while proclaiming the rights of man.

The humanitarianism of the late eighteenth century was strengthened in the nineteenth not only by the successful political revolutions in the New World and the Old, but also by the religious revival of these years. The awakening concern for the souls of the heathen in far distant lands found expression in the foreign missionary movement as well as in a renewed concern about the health of their own souls. People today who casually quote "Though every prospect pleases And only man is vile" probably do not realize that those lines come from Reginald Heber's hymn of this period. Its first verse with its mistaken geography is contemporary evidence of the interest taken in Cook's and other explorers' expeditions and in the increasing knowledge of an expanding world with all its attendant problems to consider:

> From Greenland's icy mountains,
> From India's coral strands,

Where Afric's sunny fountains
　Roll down their golden sand;
From many an ancient river,
　From many a palmy plain,
They call us to deliver
　Their land from error's chain. (1819)

The Methodist revival had deepened religious idealism. The eighteen-thirties now had, as one phase of religious thought, the Oxford Movement and Newman's conversion to Catholicism. Consciences of high-minded men and women were pricked by evil conditions in the prisons and in the insane asylums, by the crying need for protection for women and children toiling in factories created by the Industrial Revolution, and by the horrors of human slavery and of the African slave-trade. Parliament, like the Royal Society in those days, was still under the control of the old guard—Tories. The spirit of a new age was behind the Reform Law of 1832,—the first of a series of acts by which the people of Britain gradually won control over their legislature. The liberal spirit also found expression in a succession of humanitarian reforms immediately after the passage of that first Act, and was both background and stimulus for similar changes in other aspects of men's lives. This was especially true where science was concerned.

Even in the last decades of the eighteenth century liberal thinkers had been restive about the legal restrictions placed upon the education and the activities of men who were not members of the Church of England. In 1779 Protestant non-conformists had been allowed to teach without restriction except in the universities and the public schools like Eton. Annual acts of indemnity had long safeguarded dissenters from infringement of the old Test and Corporation Acts of Charles II's day. The repeal of those acts came in 1828, to be followed the next year by the Catholic Emancipation Act. Still, no one could matriculate at Oxford without first subscribing to the Thirty-Nine Articles of the Church of England. At Cambridge, the non-conformist could matriculate but he could not hold a scholarship or a fellowship, nor could he receive a university degree.

Consequently the "university" of London was founded in 1828 on a non-sectarian basis. That called forth much opposition on religious grounds and aroused the jealousy of the universities and the medical associations, thus delaying the grant to it of power to award degrees. A few years later King's College as its rival was established on Anglican principles. Finally both University College and King's were incorporated together as the University of London and empowered to hold examinations and award degrees.

Concerned by the state of affairs at the two old universities, parliament finally appointed commissions to study them. Only by the Acts of 1854 and 1856, following these reports, were matriculants freed from religious tests at Oxford and admitted to degrees. The revitalizing of these institutions in this period was marked by the adoption in Cambridge in 1848 of the Tripos in Natural Science and in Oxford two years later of the honor school in that subject. Then Oxford began the construction of its university laboratories in the next few years, while the gift of the Cavendish Laboratories to Cambridge in 1871 gave tremendous impetus to scientific work there. Until the 1850's, however, scientific growth in England was almost entirely apart from the universities as such.

Nonetheless, the sciences had been developing rapidly during these decades of continued university indifference. Lyell's *Principles of Geology,* first published in 1830, became the basis for prolonged discussions about the origins and age of the earth. Laplace in France, a mathematician-astronomer, had proposed the nebular hypothesis to explain the origins of a universe that was being constantly enlarged by observational astronomers, notably the Herschel family of father, son, and father's sister Caroline. The discovery of the planet Neptune in 1846 as the result of scientific calculations and predictions gave dramatic proof to people in general of the value of the scientific method. Dalton and the other chemists were developing the modern science on Lavoisier's consolidation of the eighteenth century discoveries of Cavendish, Priestley and their fellows. Count Rumford and the other physicists had finally disproved the fallacious theory that heat was a substance, and both chemistry and physics profited. Michael Faraday in the eighteen-thirties performed his classic experiments on the relation between electricity and magnetism, on dynamos and on electrolysis.

Invention kept pace with science. The steam-boat was soon followed by the locomotive engine and the railroads. The telegraph followed hard on the heels of the new work in electricity. Medical science applied the discoveries of the chemists in their own work and anaesthesia began its beneficent career. When antisepsis and then asepsis followed in the wake of Pasteur's studies of bacteria in the sixties, the profession of the surgeon as we know it today at last became possible.

Since this is not a history of science and technology, enough has been suggested, perhaps, to make clear that science was flourishing in England in the nineteenth century well before the universities had modernized their programs of study. Both they and the Royal Society needed to arouse themselves from the torpor into which the Society, at any rate, was sunk in the early part of this period. Ferments were at work all around them. The Society at length responded and managed to revitalize itself just before the two universities bestirred themselves. With that renewal of vitality, all three have moved again to the forefront of their respective fields.

Relations Between Science and Theology

Such advances in science and technology inevitably led to discussions of theology and philosophy, just as those of the seventeenth century had done. But this time they became more widespread and far more critical as the century wore on and the impact of the new scientific thought was more deeply realized. One indication of this rising conflict in ideas is found in the will of the Earl of Bridgewater, drawn up in 1825 and put into effect after his death four years later. A Fellow of the Royal Society himself since 1808, the Earl left £8000 to the Society's president for the author or authors who would publish books on the general theme, "On the Power, Wisdom, and Goodness of God, as manifested in the Creation," with illustrations drawn from the entire world of nature and from ancient and modern discoveries in art, science and literature. The president took counsel with the Archbishop of Canterbury and with the Bishop of London in selecting eight leading thinkers, seven of them Fellows, to write books on divisions of this subject. The Bridgewater Treatises, four of them by clergymen and four by physicians, were the result.

One is reminded at once of the seventeenth century concern with revealed religion when the telescope and the microscope were in their infancy, and of Boyle's provision in his will for an annual sermon on this general theme. Barrow, however, writing in 1849, reported that there was much criticism because one man, instead of eight, had not been asked to carry out the Earl's wishes. Also, the books were published in far too costly a form to reach any but the rich. "Never, I believe," he added, "were the intentions of a pious and benevolent testator more completely frustrated."

The arguments of these Treatises as they sought to demonstrate the existence of design in nature from particular examples by analogy, may be old-fashioned today. Indeed they may be obsolete because of the scientific advances since then; but they were notable, in spite of Barrow's comments, in the intellectual life of their day. That the struggle was severe between an earnest man's traditional beliefs about the Book of Genesis and his newly acquired geological knowledge, can be readily understood by anyone who has read Edmond Gosse's account of his own father's difficulties in these times. The intellectual and theological upheaval created by the new geology was only less in importance than that which arose in the sixties and seventies out of the Darwinian theories in biology.

Because some of these new ideas were already at work —the Geological Society, it will be recalled, had been founded in 1807—some of his associates, as "Peter Pindar" had claimed, thought Sir Joseph Banks had not sufficiently recognized the mathematicians, physicists and chemists and their increasing importance, when he considered the candidates for membership in the Society. Perhaps with this in mind, Sir Joseph had wanted Dr. William Wollaston, a noted chemist and physician, to succeed him in office.

Reform of the Society: First Step

Dr. Wollaston had been secretary for fourteen years and a councilor for seventeen. Unlike many of his colleagues, he had contributed largely to the *Philosophical Transactions*, for, an unusually expert experimenter, he had discovered palladium and rhodium. Later on he had finally learned how to make platinum malleable. But Wollaston refused to serve as president except for the few months till November. Then, probably because of his influence, Sir Humphry Davy, another scientist, succeeded him in the presidency and for the first time twelve scientists, a majority, were elected to the Council.

Thus in 1820 came the first step toward reform. Thereafter the Council never had fewer scientist members, and soon had many more. By the middle of the century they numbered on the average eighteen out of twenty-one members, and this greater concern with science led to a marked increase in the average attendance at the Council meetings.

Not only did the influence of Dr. Wollaston's brief presidency help to bring scientists into prominence in the government of the Society, but he also was the founder of its Donation Fund for the subsidizing of scientific research. This had been one of the purposes of the founders and early Fellows, as Sprat had stated,[1] a dream not to be fulfilled for nearly two centuries. Just before his death, in 1828, Dr. Wollaston gave £2000 for this purpose. The president added £1000 and other Fellows smaller sums, so that this Donation Fund, as it came to be called, totaled £3410. Its income was to be used liberally by the president and Council to promote some special research, to reward those making such researches, or to promote in some similar manner the interests of the Society in particular and of science in general. No restrictions as to nationality were made. Some fifty years later £1000 was added to the capital sum.

Nevertheless, this first half of the nineteenth century continued to be almost as barren of benefactions through the Society to science as had the eighteenth. The tide was turning, however. In the twentieth century the Society would have nearly sixty different funds and grants with thousands of pounds available annually for the furtherance of science.

Sir Humphry Davy

The election of Sir Humphry Davy to the presidency in 1820 was a tribute to the inventor of the miners' safety lamp, and also an interesting recognition of a man who, with limited education and early opportunity, had made himself outstanding in the London world of his day. Apprenticed after his father's death to a surgeon and apothecary when he was in his middle teens, he began experiments in chemistry in his bedroom with the simplest kind of apparatus. His activities won him friends who succeeded in getting Davy transferred from Penzance in Cornwall to the "Pneumatic Institution" in Bristol as a laboratory assistant. From there he went to the newly established

1 Sprat, 77-79.

Royal Institution in London in 1801 as assistant lecturer in chemistry and director of the laboratory, with living accommodations in the building, in addition to his salary. From then on his scientific work developed rapidly into work of distinction, and so also did his position in public estimation. Elected a Fellow two years after his arrival in London, he served on the Council for five years before his marriage in 1812. In that year also he was knighted by the Prince Regent.

Weld has recorded that Davy was so well known that a letter from Italy reached him though the address read simply "Siromfredevi, Londra." Unfortunately, Sir Humphry's "inordinate admiration of hereditary rank," developing in all probability out of his own inner sense of social insecurity, may have handicapped him. He was also quick, irritable and inclined to be flippant, and at the same time supercilious and haughty in his manner. At any rate, in spite of his punctual, constant attendance and his dignity in the chair, his popularity in the presidency rapidly declined and he himself was unhappy over the government's use of the Society at need and its apparent disregard of the Society's interests in general. Ill-health also grew upon him, causing him to seek relief in European travel for nearly a year before his death ended his presidency of seven years.

In his will Sir Humphry left to the Society the valuable silver service given him in recognition of his invention of the safety lamp, with the request that the service be melted down and the metal used to found a medal—the Davy Medal—to be given annually for the most important discovery in chemistry made in Europe or "Anglo-America."

Sir Humphry's dream for the Society's future as stated in his first presidential address [2] sounds like a recapitulation in brief of Sir Francis Bacon's chart for the advancement of learning two hundred years earlier. In contrast to Sir Joseph Banks' attitude of opposition, Sir Humphry began by welcoming the new scientific societies, because natural

2 Cited in Weld, II, 345-355.

science had far outgrown the capacities of one organization even to keep the records, let alone publish the research being done. He noted the recent developments and the promise for the future in mathematics and astronomy with their applications in exploration and geography; in physics and chemistry with their studies in heat, light, optics and electricity; in studies of crystallization and in animal and vegetable physiology. He concluded with a reference to the "sober and cautious method of inductive reasoning which is the germ of truth and of permanency in all the sciences," with a hope that the Society would continue to show its zeal in all this work and with an offer to help as "a private soldier" himself in the ranks of science.

In 1825 Sir Humphry Davy received notice without forewarning that King George IV wished to establish two gold medals to be awarded annually, as the president and Council should direct, as honorary premiums for the encouragement of scientific work. During the years since they were first set up, while there have been many modifications in the regulations governing these awards, these two Royal Medals have been given for the most important contributions to the advancement of natural knowledge in its two major divisions, published originally in the King's dominions within a set period of years. From 1826, with rare exceptions, to the present day, these Royal Medals have been annually awarded by the reigning sovereign to the men recommended by the Council. The roll of the recipients from Dalton on is indeed a proud one.

The government had not hesitated during these years to call upon the Society for its advice and its services in various ways. One problem presented for its consideration concerned Sir Humphry himself as a chemist,—how best to protect from corroding the copper sheathing used on the navy ships. He worked many months on the problem, finally reporting on his proposals in an elaborate paper to the Society. Almost immediately thereafter, his solution was abandoned by the Admiralty, for while the copper by

PLATE 17. Charles II, Founder and Patron, by Lely

From *The Record of the Royal Society*, London, 1940, by courtesy of the Royal
Society)

PLATE 18. The Library in Burlington House, 1910
The portrait of Charles II hung above the fireplace. Some of Newton's instrumen
were displayed on the middle table

(From *The Record of the Royal Society*, London, 1940, by courtesy of the Royal Society

his method did not corrode, it attracted such a growth of shellfish, seaweed and so forth that the fouling seriously impeded the ships. Sir Humphry was deeply mortified by this decision on the heels of his important paper. His ill-health soon became serious.

The reorganization of the Society, begun in 1820 by placing scientists in the presidency and in the majority on the Council, was carried further almost immediately thereafter by a revision of the statutes. These had not been formally altered since just before Sir Joseph Banks became president in the seventeen-seventies. Many changes had occurred since then, not least among them the shift in quarters from Crane Court to Somerset House, and the gift of the collections to the British Museum. The revisions the committee recommended and the Council adopted, raised the weekly fee from 52 shillings a year to 80 shillings or four pounds, and the admission fee to ten pounds. They also ended at this time the old custom of having the candidate sign a bond for his payments.

The problem of membership the committee barely touched, recommending only that the foreign members be limited to fifty in any one year. To be sure, since the early seventeen-sixties when the average number of these foreign members had totaled 161, they had been steadily decreasing till they numbered about forty in Sir Humphry's time. But by limiting the number elected, the committee hoped to increase the distinction of the election.

Unfortunately, at this time it was rather generally understood that any candidate proposed to the Society would be duly elected;[3] but the committee did nothing about limiting the number of Fellows. Certainly, the steady and rapid increase in their numbers lends credence to the view that all who would could join. Incidentally, these increased numbers were overcrowding the rooms assigned the Society in Somerset House, making necessary some additional space there. This the government allotted in 1826.

Dissatisfaction with the membership situation increased

3 Lyons, 244-245

and another committee for the Council undertook to consider the problem of adequate limitation. One of its members was the Mr. Babbage who became so concerned about the Society's imminent end, as he foresaw it. This second committee reported in 1827, recommending to the Council among other matters, that until the membership was reduced to a limit of four hundred, only four new members annually should be elected. This report was referred by the Council of that year to the next Council.

On this new Council under the presidency of the mathematician and geologist who had succeeded Davy, was Lord Colchester, a lawyer of long experience and Lord Chief Justice since 1816. He had been a Fellow since 1793 but had never been active in the Society's work until he was made a councilor at the new president's desire. They two, even though the president had been on the committee making the original report, succeeded in securing its rejection by this Council. The reformers had failed.

The Duke of Sussex and the Second Step

The president of the Society then arranged that his own successor in office in 1830 should be the Duke of Sussex, one of the sons of George III. Whereat the scientific Fellows in their indignation proposed John F. W. Herschel, son of the great observer and himself a noted astronomer. The Duke received eight more votes than the astronomer out of a total of 230 votes cast from a membership of 659. Again the reformers were defeated.

That year as part of this violently contested election, beside Babbage's book on *The Decline of Science*, there appeared *Science Without a Head*, published anonymously and re-issued a few years later in *The Royal Society in the Nineteenth Century*, both by Dr. A. B. Granville, as well as a pamphlet by James South, an astronomer and Fellow who had been on the original committee with Babbage. Highly critical of the Society as these writers were, as we have already seen, some of their suggestions bore fruit in the measures taken by the Councils of the next few years.

The Duke himself, though no scientist, was clear-headed and forceful about administrative detail in his first two years in office. As president he at once proposed an important change,—that the treasurer's report for the preceding year should be printed and circulated among the Fellows as a regular practice. This was the first time that any of them except the members of the Council had had the opportunity to be so informed. Fortunately the treasurer elected that year was both a distinguished mathematician and a bank director. His reports, based on a full study of the Society's administration, gave the reformers later the material with which to work.

Reaction

Dr. Granville in his history of this period, written after the fifth year of the Duke's presidency, claimed that the new president had introduced many salutary reforms during his first year or so in office, but that since he had been unable to attend the Council meetings thereafter with any degree of regularity, conditions had become even worse than before. He had not, for example, attended a single meeting of the Council or of the Society that year, and in the year before had been twice at the Society and only five times at the Council. The good work of the first two years of his administration was being buried under a renewal of the old difficulties. As Dr. Granville tactfully expressed it: certain "exceptional selections among the Councils, lead one to think, that our Royal President's heart is equally assailable, with his predecessors, by the kindly feelings of direct or indirect personal predilection, —not always the best guides to a correct discrimination of merit."

To be sure, desirable changes had been made in the

statutes, but perhaps not by the wisest method through lack of consultation with the Fellows as a whole. The library, which until then was a disgrace in its chaotic condition and its inaccessibility, had at last been catalogued, and made available to the Fellows many more hours in the week than formerly. The Arundel MSS. had been shifted to the British Museum and money had been spent on securing modern scientific books and journals.

Not only by the publication of the treasurer's report was there a marked improvement on the old system of silence and mystery, but the minutes of the Council meetings were being printed as well, and the *Proceedings* had been distributed regularly since 1830. Publication of the abstracts filed with the detailed papers printed in the *Philosophical Transactions* was another useful service,— which, incidentally, has been continued ever since; after 1904, in two series: A. Mathematical and Physical Papers, B. Biological Papers.

Unfortunately, however, the Duke's rare appearances were reflected in the slim attendance of others at the Council meetings. Nevertheless Granville refused to believe, so he said, "that His Royal Highness was governing, aided by only one or two private advisers, or under the control of a secret camarilla." But the present situation as he saw it was more oligarchic and objectionable than it had been before the Duke's election.

Whereas only seven new members had been elected in 1830, fifty new Fellows had been "made" in 1834, and thirty-three the next year. Of the 158 Fellows admitted in the past five years, only ten of them had contributed papers to the *Transactions* either before or after their election. As Dr. Granville remarked, the reader could draw his own conclusions about their scientific qualifications and about whether the situation regarding the selection of members in the past few years had improved at all.

The analysis that Granville made of these 158 new Fellows is worth summarizing to demonstrate how far the Society had yet to go before it lost its non-scientific char-

acter. These new Fellows included one bishop, nine noblemen, seven naval and seven army officers, fifteen clergymen, twelve "who are titled in the Law, learned in the
Law, or practising the Law," eighteen physicians, and
eight surgeons, and eighty other "Gentlemen" who do not
fall into any of the preceding classifications, among them
seven members of Parliament. One is inclined to under-
line Granville's query as to whether all these men were
truly "labourers in the vineyard" of science. In spite of
Granville's figures, another ten years had to pass before
this situation was corrected. In the meantime the membership continued to swell till in the 'forties it reached its
maximum size of 766.

One has to remember that the Duke was an elderly man
when he came to the presidency (he was born in 1773 and
died in 1843). Though he showed in his first anniversary
speech that he had accepted the office with every intention
of using his high social position and his best efforts to further the work of the Society faithfully and efficiently as its
"organ" and "public voice," frankly admitting his own
lack of scientific knowledge, he was able to deal with the
situation for only a year or two. Then he found his sight
too poor, his health failing, and his financial resources too
straitened to cope with all the meetings and the entertainment expected of the president.[4] He must have been dis-
heartened too by the Council's disregard of some of the
reforms he had supported, and by the excellent treasurer's
disgusted resignation after five years of struggle. But the
Duke allowed his own name to stand for re-election and
so continued as president till 1838, although vice-presidents had to act for him.

Continuing Weaknesses

This also was one of the complaints of the reformers,—
that presidents were re-elected although for months at a

[4] Lyons, 238, 256.

time they had not officiated because of ill-health or of absence abroad, or both. Such had been the case with Sir Joseph Banks in his last years, with Sir Humphry Davy and now with the Duke. Not for a hundred years more was the president's term limited by statute; but after a time four or five years became the customary term. Since 1820, only two presidencies have been for as long as ten years. From 1870 until the emergency of World War II, no president has served for longer than five years, and some, for various reasons, have not been in office as long as that. Thus one reform took effect through precedent rather than by legislation. Finally in 1935 the Council set the president's term at five years.

Another matter rightly troubling the reformers, Granville noted, at the time of the Duke's presidency was the editing of the *Philosophical Transactions*. Since 1752 this had been done under the direction of the Council through its Committee on Papers with the officers and vice-presidents as permanent members and with the secretaries in direct charge. This committee was authorized to call upon specialists whenever necessary, but no paper had been so referred in the fifty years between 1780 and 1831. The quorum for the committee was only seven and some of these men were not even scientists. Were the papers wisely chosen or rejected? Furthermore, the number of papers had greatly increased. Only 319 had been presented in the seventeen-nineties; less than fifty years later the number presented had more than doubled. In 1831 and 1832 consultation became the rule, only to lapse again. Permanent reform had to await a reorganized Society.

In this connection the Reverend William Whewell made some interesting comments when he was asked to make suggestions about the founding of the British Association at York in 1831. Dr. Whewell had been made a Fellow in 1820 at the age of twenty-six, a year after he had published his *Elementary Treatise on Mechanics*. He had been placed on the Council in the first year of the presidency of the Duke of Sussex, but he was too busy at that time with his Bridgewater Treatise and his *History of the Inductive Sciences* to accept the Duke's invitation to serve on a committee to revise the Society's statutes. Ten years later he became Master of Trinity College, Cambridge.

In September, 1831, Dr. Whewell wrote suggesting that the proposed British Association limit membership to those "who have published *written papers* in the memoirs of any learned society." "It would be desirable," he went on, "in some way to avoid the crowd of lay members whose names stand on the list of the Royal Society." Further, the Committee on memoirs for the British Association should "*give public* reports of their views. Neglect of this practice appears to me to be a serious deficiency in the Royal Society." For the Royal Society's committee merely used in the minutes "certain laconic formulae of expression," as Granville charged, ordering a paper "postponed," "to be printed," "to be placed in the archives," or "not to be printed," without "one particle of reason or ground being alleged, at the same time, for the recorded decision of the committee." No wonder Whewell advocated written reports on each paper that the new British Association might consider for publication.

Under the Duke's administration in the early eighteen-thirties, the organization of the Society had been tightened up in a number of respects; but unfortunately, the impetus for continuing these changes soon died down. The particular change of major importance and the permanent achievement of this period was the publication of the Society's business and especially of its financial reports. This was the second outstanding reform; hereafter the Fellows at large and not just the Council had facts at their disposal.

The Final Major Reform

The leader of the third and final major reform was Mr. R. W. Grove, the eminent mathematician and physicist, the inventor of the Grove battery and the holder of a Royal Medal (1847). He was also a lawyer, and ultimately became Queen's Counsel and a judge. He was knighted in 1871. Mr. Grove came on the Council five years after he had been elected a Fellow in 1840, and at once joined the reforming group. These men thought that a revision of the ancient Charters would be necessary to change the Society's character. As a member of the Charter Committee to study possible amendments, Mr. Grove was the one who proposed instead an alteration of the existing method of electing the Fellows. In other words, he had put his finger on the root difficulty of the Society's troubles, a difficulty that now could be solved since the Council after 1820 had had scientists in the majority, and since the treasurer's reports, published since 1830, provided the figures with which to work.

The Charter Committee was not long in reporting to the Council nor the Council long in setting up procedures within the old Charters that accomplished the desired results in due time. These procedures were that the election of new Fellows should be made only once a year, instead of at any and every meeting, that the Council should recommend to the Society the most eligible candidates, and that such candidates should not exceed fifteen in number. When these regulations were approved and distributed to the Fellows early in 1847, the way was clear for the Royal Society to develop into a scientific association. Mr. Grove's suggestion worked.

Since a good deal has been said about the interweaving of finances with the membership problem because of the Society's dependence upon the members' fees, it should be added here that the Charter Committee, before making its recommendations, had studied the treasurer's figures and had made tentative budgets to determine whether the Society could afford the cut in income that would come when new members each year were less than half the number elected in previous years. The ordinary Fellows would, of course, decline in number as deaths and resignations exceeded the number of admissions. Thus by natural attrition the number of non-scientific members would dwindle and, through the Council's selection of scientists as new Fellows, they would not be replaced.

That is what has happened. By 1901 only three Fellows remained who had been elected before 1848. Since 1875 the average number of ordinary Fellows in any five-year period has been less than five hundred.

These restrictions in number, however, did not apply to the special classifications of royal or noble Fellows. Nor in theory, at least, were the Fellows debarred at any time from electing whom they chose, as they were privileged to do by the Charters. But as in so many other cases, orderly procedures once accepted with the weight of precedent and custom added, have become tantamount to legislative change without the onerous difficulties involved in bringing about amendments to fundamental laws.

The Philosophical Club

Mr. William Grove did not relax his oversight of the Society's well-being when once the Council had adopted the Committee's recommendations. He and a group of like-thinking Fellows organized a dining-club in 1847, the "Philosophical Club" with forty-seven members in honor of the year in which the reform was accomplished. Their purpose was to watch over the Council's policies and to stimulate it to develop the Society's major concerns. It is said that many proposals arising out of their discussions were later adopted by various Councils.

Some fifty or more years later, its work over, the Club ended its separate existence (1901) by joining forces with the ancient Royal Society Club. This in its turn had originated out of the custom some of the first Fellows had established of dining together in a tavern after the weekly meetings. In 1743 this informal practice was made more regular by the organization of what after 1795 was known as the Royal Society Club. They had always entertained guests freely at these dinners, so that these occasions were notable both for their social aspect and for their discussions. In the nineteenth century the Club had become wholly social. That was why the reforming Fellows had felt the need of a new club for a specific purpose. After their purposes had been accomplished, the forty-seven members could merge themselves with the other, older group.

Reform Within and Without the Society

When one observes the Society's stagnation in the early days of the nineteenth century while British science itself was making great strides, one is impressed by the coincidence in time between the Society's reorganization and the great reform movements in politics and in social affairs that came to a head in the thirties and forties. The Society was indeed a part of the life of its times and could not remain unaffected, unless it were to wither away, crowded out by its own slack conservatism, by the rapid development of the specialized societies and by the new British Association for the Advancement of Science. It too was reinvigorated and re-modeled in those same decades, by the scientist Fellows who found that the old organization of the seventeenth century could be adapted successfully to new ideas two hundred years later.

By the middle of the nineteenth century, the "unhappy period" of the Society's history had been brought to a fortunate conclusion. Science in England was far from declining or from being without a head. In fact, the specialized sciences were developing so rapidly that new organizations were inevitably called into being to meet their needs. The Royal Society as patrons and lovers of science for two hundred years could no longer maintain the honorable position of leadership of its earlier years or serve as a center for the country's scientific work without drastic reorganization. But it had the strength and the vitality as well as the leadership within its own membership to reorganize itself and so to confound its critics. Then, once more, backed by its long history and the prestige of its past, it resumed its ancient position of leadership, this time as an association of the most distinguished scientists from all fields, to serve as a kind of general council and spokesman for the common interests of all the more specialized groups. Its record of achievement during the hundred years since 1847 amply refutes the false prophecies of its imminent end in the eighteen-thirties.

13

NEW GROWTH

THE MAJOR ADMINISTRATIVE changes accomplished between 1820 and 1847 made possible the development of the Society into its present position of power and responsibility. But that development was not achieved in a day, nor indeed for several decades. Reorganization had to reach into many aspects of the Society's interests beside that of the selection of candidates for membership. Other changes varied of course in their importance, and most of them now, perhaps, are of interest only to those intimately concerned with the administration of the Society's affairs. One or two, however, are worth noting here, because by implication they provide further evidence of the unfortunate conditions the Society has had to overcome. One reform already mentioned indicated the neglect and disuse into which the Society's remarkable collection of books had fallen. Since 1831, all that has been altered and an active Library Committee has maintained supervision to assure the library's continued growth.

An irretrievable loss occurred sometime between 1800 and 1830, although the Society's attention was not called to that fact until twenty-five years later. When the keen-eyed old Dutchman, Leeuwenhoek, died in 1723, he left his invaluable collection of high-powered microscope lenses, like solitaire diamonds, to the Royal Society that had welcomed his letters about his discoveries of little "animalcules"—bacteria—and had made him a foreign member more than forty years earlier. Somehow unaccountably that collection of lenses had disappeared from the Society's rooms. So also had the clock given to the Society by Dr. Seth Ward early in the sixteen-sixties in memory of a Gresham professor and fellow virtuoso, Laurence Rooke. Rooke, friend of the virtuosi and for many years their host at Gresham College, had died before the Society's formation, or he would have been one of the foremost in it. It was his chair of geometry that the young Christopher Wren had been brought from Oxford to London to occupy just before the Restoration.

Although the Society regretted these losses and records were set up of its other possessions, the officers waited yet longer, until the twentieth century, to set up controls. Now the records are regularly checked so that objects on temporary loan or stored away are not overlooked or forgotten.

To cope with its increased cares, the Council either reactivated old regular or standing committees such as the ones for finance and the library, or in the course of the years set up new ones, in addition to the special committees used for particular problems. As some of these committees now did not have even one councilor as a member, the Fellows in general gradually became more familiar with and more active in the Society's business, in contrast to that recent period in its history when Granville had declared that the Society was ruled by a "Venetian oligarchy."

The Soirées

Not exactly the reform of an abuse, but still significant as an indication of a changed attitude, was the custom
of welcoming large numbers of guests, established in 1849
and continued ever since. In that year the Council decided
to invite people to an evening *soirée* or *conversazione,* as
they are still called, to mingle among the Fellows and to
observe displays about recent scientific work. In other
words, the growth of the separate scientific groups had become so important that the Council of the Royal Society felt
it necessary to modify its club-like atmosphere and to receive within its rooms a large number of invited guests.
It had awakened to the need for a wider and better understanding of the Society's purposes and activities.

Originally these soirées were at the personal expense of
the president in whose name the guests were invited. After
1871 they were made the responsibility of the Society.
These semi-social occasions evidently served a useful function for they still occur about twice a year. Usually about
five hundred guests are invited. They are formally received
by the president and his wife, the beautiful mace there on
a table beside them. Not only do the guests then have an
opportunity to meet the distinguished members and to
hear their explanations of the displays, but they can also
study the Society's many portrtaits of famous Fellows that
line the stairways as well as the rooms. They may see also
Charles II himself gazing down upon them from Lely's
large painting in the meeting-room. (Plate 17.)

Burlington House

In the early days of these soirées, the Society had to
borrow space for them from other organizations who were
its neighbors in Somerset House. This situation pointed
up the necessity for securing more room for the Society

itself, for its swollen ranks, still almost at their maximum number, would not shrink to the desired five hundred or less for forty years and more. Then came the immensely successful Exhibition held in 1851 in Hyde Park, with its emphasis on the part played by science in modern life. At the suggestion of Prince Albert, Queen Victoria's consort, the profits from the Exhibition were used to purchase undeveloped land in South Kensington where it was proposed to establish a center for the scientific societies. They, however, preferred a more central location. The Royal Society, as spokesman for the group, secured government consent for the use of Burlington House on Piccadilly. At length the Society was again assuming its old position of leadership.

In 1856 the Royal Society moved from Somerset House to Burlington House, to be joined there by the Linnean and the Chemical Societies, as well as the British Association. In 1873 the Society was finally established in its present rooms,—in a wing of the main House, facing the court between the House itself and the street.

Funds From the Government

The improvements within the Society during the 'thirties and 'forties did not pass unobserved outside. As a result there came an expansion of its responsibilities as well as of its activities along two lines,—first, through a marked increase in the funds entrusted to it for the promotion of research, and second, through the development of its relations with other scientific organizations, both national and international.

The first welcome recognition by the government of the Society's new growth came in an unexpected letter from Lord John Russell to the president. In it he proposed a government grant in aid of scientific investigation. A committee of the Society at once drew up a report recommending four uses for such a grant; to aid private individual research, to help in the study of masses of accumulated observations, to purchase new instruments for astronomical, meteorological and other observations, and, subordinately, to assist such other scientific investigations or purposes that might become desirable. The recommendations were adopted and the £1000 granted in 1850 were followed by similar awards for the next five years.

Then the government decided that the special services fund would not admit of such an annual grant, even though the Society pointed out that it was an award for the furtherance of science and not a subsidy to an organization. Thereafter the grant was included in the sums voted annually by parliament, and as such was administered by the Society through a committee of Fellows and the presidents of four other scientific groups.

Some twenty years later an experimental assignment of £4000 annually for a five year period was set up as a "Government Fund" which could be used for personal allowances to those making the investigations. This Fund was under the Science and Art Department of the government and was administered by the same general committee of the Society, enlarged, however, by the presidents of a number of other societies and academies. Also, sub-committees were set up in charge of the mathematical and physical sciences, biology, chemistry, and "general purposes."

Again the question arose whether this Fund was an award to the Royal Society or a grant for the furthering of science. The Society wanted it made very clear that it was for the latter purpose. The statement for Parliament's consideration as finally adopted was "Royal Society. Grant for Scientific Investigation undertaken with the sanction of a Committee appointed for the purpose." The original grant of £1000 was no longer to be awarded; but £4000 was thereafter annually appropriated to be used primarily for investigations but also, if necessary, for personal allowances. Various matters in connection with this annual grant were adjusted from time to time, but until the twentieth century brought increases in the amounts granted, no fundamental changes were made.

The government was not subsidizing the Society except by housing it rent-free as it had done since 1780. By these grants, however, it recognized the Society's leadership by making it the administrator of government aid to science and to scientists. The advice of the representatives from the other learned bodies was specifically limited to the selection of the persons to be aided, the amounts to be granted and the terms of the grants. To cover its expenses for this work, the Society at first received only small sums each year. When the annual grant was increased to £7000 in 1936, the amount paid the Society for expenses was £350.

Funds From Private Sources

Funds came to the Society, also, for other than direct aid for scientific research. For example, one of the reforming Fellows, perhaps moved by the humanitarian spirit of the age, proposed in 1859 that a Scientific Relief Fund should be set up to aid scientists and their families where necessary. This proposal with the backing of the Philosophical Club received the support of the Council and then of the Society and was set up at once with gifts totaling more than £3000. The fund has grown rapidly since, so that the committee in charge has an annual income of more than £800 with which to give aid. Other provision in similar fashion has been made for a variety of purposes that range from a pension fund for the staff of the Society to a fund to provide scientific books in braille for the blind. By 1940 there were twenty-four of these special funds, including those for lectures. They totaled £109,941.

Endowments for the award of medals as prizes, begun with the Copley Fund in the early eighteenth century were continued with the Rumford Medal just before 1800. In the nineteenth century these awards rapidly increased in number. First came the Davy Medal, and then the two Royal ones. Four more followed in fairly quick succession. Finally the Council resolved in 1900 not to accept any more funds for such purposes. It was neither to the advantage of the Society nor in the interests of the advancement of natural knowledge to add to the number of the awards already provided for.

More important, and most markedly so in recent years, has been the growth of the financial resources entrusted to the Society to administer for the encouragement of scientific work. This swelling tide of funds is indeed a tribute to the recognition given science today and to the respect in which the Society's judgments are held. Dr. Wollaston's legacy of the Donation Fund in 1829 has proved to be the forerunner of many more thousands of pounds that have come to the Society from private sources, especially as the nineteenth century drew to a close, and as the twentieth century illustrated the importance of science in the modern world.

When Sir Henry Lyons, treasurer of the Society for ten years, ended his term of office in 1939, he recorded that the Society had a General Purposes Fund of £116,556 and twenty-seven Research Funds whose capital value was £555,828. In addition, it had £94,180 in income from various research funds that had not yet been used and was temporarily invested. The outstanding fact about these large amounts for the promotion of research was that they represented, he said, a tenfold increase in twenty years' time.

It is indeed a strikingly different situation now from the one that confronted the Council in 1674. For in that year arrears were so serious and members so few at the Society's meetings that the Council was hard pressed to find ways to finance "entertaining" experiments that would attract the members again and renew their interest in the work.

Nor have all the funds at the disposal of the Society today been mentioned. In addition, since the first grant of

226

£1000 was made by the government in 1850 to be used by the Society for the encouragement of research, thousands more have been assigned. Parliament now places under the Society's supervision and administration annual grants not only for scientific investigations but also for publications and for international research associations and scientific congresses.

Though in his *History* he did not specifically say so, one realizes by the dates Sir Henry Lyons gives that it was only as recently as during his term of office as treasurer, that the administration of the Society's finances was modernized. One of the longstanding difficulties recently cleared away was the transfer, completed in 1939, of Bishop Wilkins' legacy invested in fee-farm rents in 1674, —a story that has already been told. Another was the writing off as uncollectible the heavy debt accumulated during the publication of the *Catalogue of Scientific Papers,* about which more later.

The power released by these sums is far more important than a mere enumeration of them. The record, however, does illustrate clearly the contrast between the Society's position after it had shaped itself into an organization capable of carrying out its original purpose, and its position in the early years when it was solely dependent upon the weekly shillings reluctantly paid by its members. What has been done with some of these funds in the past fifty years can be read in the titles and the size of some of the Society's publications. For example, among others it has issued a series of reports by its Malaria Commission, and by its Commissions on Sleeping Sickness and on Mediterranean Fever. It has published five quarto volumes on the work of the National Antarctic Expedition of 1901-4. Some other reports published have been studies made by individual scientists like that by J. C. Beattie of a magnetic survey of South Africa and one on *The Sub-Mechanics of the Universe* by O. Reynolds. The policy of publication that the Society began in the seventeenth century has been continued in the nineteenth and twentieth centuries. The subjects named also give a hint of the wide range of the Society's interests.

Cooperation, National and International

The second characteristic of the reorganized Society's activities is the rapid and marked development of its leadership in relation to other scientific organizations at home and abroad. Increasingly these others have called upon the Society to take over responsibility, to give advice or to provide the spear-head for a generally desired action. Thus, even a hundred years ago, it had represented other organizations besides itself when it sought permission of the government to be quartered in Burlington House rather than at South Kensington. Later on, the British Association transferred to the Society its responsibility for the Kew Observatory and, later still, proposed that the Society join with the Association in securing government support for the organization of the National Physical Laboratory. As a result, the Laboratory was opened at Bushy House in Teddington in 1902 with ultimate control placed with the president and Council of the Society. Associated with their representatives on the governing board, were representatives selected by the leading technical institutions of the country. With the rapid growth of the Laboratory's work and with the formation of the government's own Department of Science and Industry, responsibility for the National Laboratory was later transferred to the government, while the Society's representatives continue to serve both on its board and its executive committee.

The Society was also called upon to share in the direction of education when the reformers of the mid-nineteenth century reached into the two old universities, and when the so-called public schools accepted the "modern" subjects of science, modern history and modern languages as part of their programs. Since 1868 the Society has had its representatives on the governing boards of some of the important schools. Nine of them now, including Eton, Winchester and Westminster, have one of their directors or trustees selected by the Council. In addition, the Society has a voice in the election of eight of the professors of science at Oxford and of one at Cambridge. Its representatives chosen by the Council, or the president ex officio, are on the boards of more than thirty other institutions, councils, funds and committees ranging from the Hunterian Museum and the Royal Veterinary College to the Science Abstracts Committee.

Still more specifically, between 1900 and 1939, the Council has subsidized from its various funds the work of 110 students, fellows and professors for periods ranging from one to many years. Included in the list of scientists aided in this way are some foreigners who have been privileged to do their research with British help.

The Society in promoting natural knowledge in many ways now works through education by subsidies to individuals as well as to institutions, through oversight of training as well as through the investigation of specific problems. Furthermore, it recognizes that science knows no political boundaries.

International cooperation in the scientific field was a rapid and logical development in the nineteenth century, especially in the latter part. Count von Humboldt, the explorer and geographer, had succeeded early in the century in securing government support from a number of countries for a series of meteorological stations throughout the globe. The Duke of Sussex, as president, had given his support to the Count's proposal that stations be set up in the British possessions also. This first notable instance of international governmental cooperation for science on a wide scale was quickly followed by many others in which the Society shared with advice and with the selection of delegates. Whether the problem was one of a common standard for weights and measures, the coordination of geodetic measures that particularly concerned the delimitation of the frontiers of newly formed states in Europe, or problems of gravitational observations, the Council did its part in securing governmental support and in recommending delegates.

The Catalogue of Scientific Papers

A major undertaking which concerned the Society for nearly three quarters of a century began as a friendly service undertaken at the request of a fellow association. It developed into an international enterprise with wide ramifications. This was the *Catalogue of Scientific Papers* that had appeared in the journals issued since 1800 by the various scientific bodies in Europe and America. First suggested by an American in 1855 for the mathematical and physical science publications only, the British Association adopted the idea and asked for the Society's cooperation. The Society undertook the task, enlarging the *Catalogue* to include all the sciences. Intended at first to be in manuscript form only, by 1864 the *Catalogue* was thought worth printing. Government help was secured, and from 1866 to 1872, there appeared the volumes covering the years from 1800 to 1863. Supplementary volumes were issued twice later, which brought the *Catalogue* through 1883.

No wonder that with its own activities, with this *Catalogue* work and with the steady decline in membership and so of fees, the Society was financially troubled for some years in the 'seventies. The funds received at this time from the sale of the Acton lands came at a particularly opportune moment; for as unrestricted capital, the income proved most useful in helping meet expenses.

The *Catalogue* needed to be continued. By this time, however, it had far outgrown the resources of the Society while it had become of great international value. The Society led the way, therefore, through a series of conferences and meetings, to the formation of an International Convention and Council for an International Catalogue. The Society offered its financial backing for the first five years from 1900, serving as the publisher, until the various cooperating national bodies could repay these advances. The agreements, twice renewed and expanded, ran through the first year of the War of 1914-18.

In 1916 the work was suspended until after the war. When the question of its resumption was considered in the light of the Society's heavy expense and labor and the failure of supporting associations to repay the loans advanced, or of subscribers to pay their considerable arrears, the International Council through its executive committee in 1922 decided to end the project. The treasurer of the Royal Society acted as receiver to close out the accounts. Few of the debts were paid. In consequence in 1935 the Society wrote off about £14,000 of the indebtedness as lost. Part of the trouble had arisen from the mistaken impression abroad that the Society was spending government funds, not its own private resources, and that the government would make good the losses! Similar societies and academies on the continent were of course governmentally supported and were not private organizations as is the Royal Society.

The International Research Council

There was other cooperation with the academies in foreign lands. Shortly before 1900, the Royal Society accepted an invitation to attend a meeting of representatives from the scientific associations of a number of German cities. The Council, however, emphasized to its delegates that the Society's adherence to any plan would depend upon its being a true international assembly with representatives from other countries. The German group thereupon consulted the Academy of Science in Berlin, while the Royal Society sounded out the academies in Paris, St. Petersburg, Rome and Washington. The first International Association of Academies met in Paris in 1900. But some of these learned societies had two sections, one scientific, the other literary. Others, like the Royal Society, were limited to the one interest, science, and could only belong to that one section and have but the one voice there. Since there was at that time no general academy in Great Britain, some proposed that the Society develop such a division of its own. Prolonged discussion followed with the Society finally deciding not to spread its interests to include the humanities.

Later on in 1901, some of the participants in that discussion, with others, organized the British Academy for the Promotion of Historical, Philosophical and Philological Studies, which received a royal charter the next year. Again, one of the proposals in the minds of the first Fellows for the Society more than two hundred years earlier had shown its far-reaching vitality, even though it was now set aside as definitely beyond the Society's field of interest and activity. The Royal Society welcomed the formation of the British Academy, securing its recognition in the International Association of Academies, as well as providing it with a meeting-place in its own rooms for more than twenty-five years, until the government made separate provision.

The International Association of Academies had to come to a close with the first World War, though various countries tried during those war years to keep some of its projects alive. With the end of the war arose the question of resumption. One difficulty in the original organization was that in some countries there had been more than one academy, and in Germany there were five academies. Consequently, matters under discussion in the International Association had taken on an undesirable political aspect. When the war was over, representatives from the French and the American Academies, meeting first with the Royal Society and then in Paris, summoned in Brussels in 1919 a conference for delegates from the Academies in all the

Allied countries. A committee meanwhile prepared a draft constitution for these delegates to consider.

The first General Assembly of the International Research Council was thus convened. Under it were organized at that meeting various International Unions,—for astronomy, for chemistry, and so on,—with others to be formed at the next triennial meeting of the International Council. Units of payment from one to eight, according to their respective populations, were to be subscribed by each participating country. The various Unions were to have autonomy in their own affairs under the International Council. In 1922 the neutral countries of the war years were invited to join, and other Unions were approved. Three years later, an invitation to the Central Powers to join was proposed and defeated under conditions that made the issue seem political. The Royal Society, dissatisfied, demanded a special General Assembly the next year to reconsider the matter. At this session the invitation was approved and extended, but it was not accepted.

The eight Unions finally organized under the International Council have carried on their work with varying degrees of regularity and of success. One, the Union of Mathematics, held two or three congresses, then disbanded in 1932. Another, the Union of Geodesy and Geophysics, split into seven sections which became practically independent associations. To avoid any political coloring, the original agreement had been that there would be no permanent bureau set up in any country. But Paris, Strasbourg and Naples have each had one for a geological field,—geodesy, seismology and volcanology respectively— and have aroused some criticism on political grounds. The Unions of Chemistry and of Astronomy, on the other hand, have been very active and successful. Through the various congresses held under the auspices of the individual Unions, scientists from many countries have come together and have done much valuable work.

The Pilgrim Trust Lecture

In 1937, Sir William Bragg in his presidential address to the annual meeting of the Royal Society announced plans for another form of international cooperation. Officers of the Society and of the National Academy of Sciences in Washington had suggested that each organization should invite a distinguished scientist from the other group to give a lecture before it in alternate years. The Pilgrim Trust in England had agreed to provide 250 guineas a year for six years as a test period in the hope that the Pilgrim Trust Lecture might ultimately become a permanent activity of the two groups. Sir William stated that the object of the Lecture would be the progress of science, not the honoring of scientists. He hoped that the Lectures would not be mere summaries of past work nor general discussions of scientific advances, but a transfer from one side of the Atlantic to the other of new ideas which had already begun to be fruitful and which promised wide expansion in the future. Natural knowledge, he went on, pays least attention to the divisions of men; "there is only one Nature for us to know. No greater gift could be made by one people to another than an illuminating idea; it would deserve a people's welcome."

At the invitation of the Royal Society, Dr. Irving Langmuir of the Research Laboratories of the General Electric Company in Schenectady gave the first Pilgrim Trust Lecture in December, 1938 before the Society in the amphitheater of the Royal Institution. His subject was Molecular Films. The editors of *Nature* held that it amply fulfilled Sir William's statement of the Lecture's purpose, and added: "Thus the first link in another chain binding together the peoples of Great Britain and the United States has been well forged." They considered such international contacts of vital importance in those days of strife and world unrest and held that every effort should be made to promote active cooperation between science workers.

The second Lecture, given before the National Academy in Washington, in April, 1939, was by Sir William Bragg himself at the invitation of the Academy. He spoke on History in the Archives of the Royal Society. He brought out the connections between the Society and America during the past centuries and indicated how the archives also illustrate the continuous endeavors of a body of scientists to be of help to their fellow men. He held that it is the obligation of science to make sure that what is found is understood, and that mated with it is the understanding of what science is doing and can do which a good education provides. Thus scientists and the general public work together for the common good. With characteristic idealism, he concluded that the spirit in which knowledge is sought is more important than the knowledge itself.

Again a World War interrupted such international cooperation and fraternization. Whether the Lectures will be resumed and how far the International Council and the Unions may progress in the years immediately following this war remain to be seen. Hunger at home, inflated currencies and high costs, added to the political use of scientific discoveries like the chaining of atomic energy, do not encourage international exchanges by scientists. Even so, the summer of 1947 saw the meeting of a number of international associations or of their councils, all seeking to close the gaps in their common work and in their relationships caused by six years of global warfare. Every such meeting should draw tighter the web of mutual understanding and respect among the men and women who now find themselves inhabitants of a world that hourly grows more interdependent.

14

THE ROYAL SOCIETY
IN RECENT YEARS

MORE THAN a hundred years have elapsed since
the Society began its transformation. From a
club-like organization of important people interested in science, of whom only one in three was himself
a scientist, it has grown into an association of the leading
British scientists. In its membership now, only a handful
of the distinguished men are not scientists themselves.
They are there because in some way they have been of
important service to science.

The change came by evolution rather than by revolution and took a good many years to become fully effective.
As late as 1860 there were 330 Fellows who were scientists
and 300 who were not. Also, in 1860, 117 of that group of
330 scientist Fellows were physicians and surgeons, an
overwhelming proportion of medical men which had been
characteristic of the Society's membership from the first.
The growth of the Society's work and the rapid develop-

ment of the newer fields of science have since then strikingly modified that situation. In 1940 the physicists and the chemists formed the two largest single groups, 86 and 79 respectively, while the Fellows working primarily in medicine numbered only 28. However, there were 94 working in fields closely related to medicine, such as physiology, pharmacology and bacteriology. It is clear that the two-hundred year old predominance of medical men has long since ended and the scientists in newer fields have increased proportionately.

By 1875 the decline in the number of Fellows, since the limited annual elections failed to replace those who had resigned or died, had brought the Society's membership down below 500 and there, between 400 and 500, it has stayed. At the same time the average age at admission to membership has slowly but steadily risen from about 40 in 1810 to a median age some years ago of about 47. The men elected nowadays have already achieved distinction, and are not the unknown young men at whom Steele, John Hill and the dissidents of 1784 jeered.

Since 1874, when the privilege was ended, peers are no longer admitted in a special class, nor, since 1902, are privy councilors. But at that later time, provision was made for the election of men "who had rendered conspicuous service to the cause of science or are such that their election would be of signal benefit to the Society." No more than two such elections may be made in any one year, and if two are made, then the following year none may be elected. In 1940 there were ten such specially elected members, while all the rest were scientists.

Among the distinguished members elected within the last seventy-five years have been such notable figures as Gladstone and Disraeli, Asquith and Baldwin, Ramsay MacDonald, Churchill and Smuts, John D. Rockefeller and Lord Nuffield,—the last two as businessmen whose philanthropies have notably furthered the medical and physical sciences. The election of Princess Elizabeth early in the summer of 1947 is a reminder that the privileged election of "the blood royal" was not rescinded when an end was made to that of the peers; but it also is a symbol of the present situation in regard to women as Fellows.

Women as Fellows

The question of the eligibility of women as members was raised in the first years of the present century and was answered in the negative. One of the benefits of the parliamentary legislation passed in behalf of women after the first World War was to remove this legal ineligibility, —but no elections ensued. Finally, at the close of the second World War, in 1945, the Council included on its approved list of candidates the names of two women: Kathleen Lonsdale (London) a physicist at the Royal Institution, for her "outstanding contributions to the investigation of the crystalline structure of organic compounds by means of X-ray analysis," and Marjory Stephenson (Cambridge) a member of the staff of the Medical Research Council, "for her biochemical researches upon the metabolism of bacteria, which, with those of her pupils during twenty-five years, have included work upon hydrogenase, lactic dehydrogenase and adaptive enzymes." (Shades of Samuel Pepys and his fears about the Duchess of Newcastle!)

Sir Henry Dale, president of the Society during those war years, reported in his annual address that autumn, that as many as ten per cent of the Fellows had opposed the election of women when a clarification of the statutes had been sought by postal vote; nevertheless, these women were elected. Dr. Agnes Arber, the distinguished botanist and historian of science received the same honor the next year, and three more women were elected in 1947. To these six women Fellows now is added a seventh, for Princess Elizabeth, heiress to the British throne, has signed the Charter-book as did James, Duke of York, as heir to Charles II.

Various Changes

In his address in 1945, Sir Henry Dale expressed his own satisfaction at having been instrumental, when secretary of the Society, in securing an increase in 1931 in the number of Fellows to be elected—from the long-standing fifteen to seventeen, and then, six years later, to twenty. As none of the forebodings aroused by these increases had materialized, he was happy to see the number for 1946 and thereafter increased to twenty-five. He foresaw no loss of prestige but a gain in vigor. Also, though this Sir Henry did not mention, the number of scientists in these days has mightily increased, and the size of the Royal Society could well be permitted to reach just over, rather than just under 500 members. For comparative purposes it is interesting to observe that the membership of the British Association, in spite of the strains of the war and post-war years, in 1947 numbered about 4000.

Marked as has been the progress of the Royal Society, once it was reorganized, the Fellows still on occasion become restive under the regulations that give the Council with the officers great power. As recently as in 1933 ninety-one Fellows made a series of proposals that have extended the active participation of the Fellows in its business. Some of the recommendations the Council accepted in 1935, others it refused, and the Society as a whole at its annual meeting that year upheld the decisions of the Council. These were, among others, to make statutory the custom that the president should hold office for not more than five years, that the tenure of the treasurer and of the secretaries should be limited to ten years, and that of the foreign secretary to five; that the outgoing Council should continue to nominate the incoming officers to the Society for election; and that the list of candidates recommended by the Council for election to that body would continue to be limited to the number of the vacancies to be filled.

The ancient Charters remain unaltered and the Society, adapting itself within their limitations, advances without losing step with its past.

One interesting consequence of a valuable change in procedures is reflected in material ways. The flow of important papers, some of them exceedingly abstruse, had tripled in number by the end of the nineteenth century. The problem was how to handle them in ways most useful to the Fellows, especially as some of these papers were so specialized as to appeal only to a few. Gradually, in recent years, instead of having a series of them read, some of these perhaps "by title" only, the custom has developed of having an important subject discussed in a long session. These discussions may begin in the morning and carry on through the afternoon. The old benches in the assembly-room were too uncomfortable for such prolonged use, so in 1939 the room was re-equipped. (See Plates 19 and 20.) Again, the Society in holding discussions for long hours has returned to the original practice of its first years.

Similarly, an early practice abandoned almost at once, then renewed early in the nineteenth century to be again abandoned, was resumed late in that century and has been continued ever since. This was the custom of appointing committees for the individual sciences and their special interests. There had been eight of these set up in 1665. In 1838, eight again were appointed, which were reduced to seven the following year as meteorology was combined with physics; but these ceased in 1849 when they were not reappointed. Finally in 1896 the Council set up sectional committees which have been continued ever since. It is through these sections that the conference discussions, noted earlier, are arranged, for the members of the sections of course have a specialized knowledge in common, and can best cooperate in worthwhile discussions which might bore a listener from a different field. Again the practice of the first days has proved useful in this modern age, making one suppose that either the seventeenth century

PLATE 19. The Meeting Room in Burlington House, as it was in 1912
(From *The Record of the Royal Society*, London, 1940, by courtesy of the Royal Society)

PLATE 20. The Meeting Room in Burlington House, 1939
The room has been stripped of its pictures for the war period

(From *The Record of the Royal Society*, London, 1940, by courtesy of the Royal Society)

and the twentieth had much in common, or that the Original Fellows were more than two centuries ahead of their times!

A Central Scientific Center?

One of the subjects discussed for several years by the members of the Philosophical Club after it was organized in 1847 was the possibility of a common meeting-place for the "major" scientific associations, combined with the advantages of a central library. The fact that Somerset House would soon be no longer available for the societies and was too crowded anyway, gave relevance to their deliberations. Apparently, the proposals were dropped after the suggested site in South Kensington seemed undesirable and the Royal Society moved into Burlington House.

The question came up again nearly fifty years ago when the Royal Society was finding itself cramped for space in its rooms along the side of Burlington House court. It had no large room for meetings and no room for expansion; nor did the other scientific societies also housed on one or the other side of the court. Besides, they all missed the advantage of a central library. Efforts at that time to secure more space failed, and the Royal Society is still in the same quarters.

Now with the rebuilding of London following World War II, Sir Henry Dale, the Society's president during those war years, has revived the old dream of a centrally located center for all the major scientific associations. When he spoke of it in 1945, the Physicists had no home at all, the Chemists with nearly 5000 members had limited accommodations. If one adds to these only the "major" groups like the Geologists, the Astronomers, and the Linnean Society, one begins to have some conception of the magnitude of the idea, and also of its potentialities. Maybe, before the Royal Society reaches its three hundredth anniversary in 1962, this dream will be on the way to becoming an actuality. For to Sir Henry, the Royal Society together with the others grown from and around it, forms "a scientific organism which is a national and imperial heritage. Here are the roots of the spreading tree of science and technology."

The War Years

Immediately before the outbreak of World War II, the officers of the Society had seen the storm arising and had made preparations accordingly. By July, 1939, the valuable portraits had been taken down and placed in safekeeping and the archives with the Charter-book and the journal-books had been crated and sent off to Wales, there to stay till all danger was over. The mace was to follow as soon as a meeting later in the month was over. Headquarters for the Society itself were to be in Cambridge for the duration. However, this move put into effect in September, 1939, lasted only for a few months. In March, 1940, the Society's headquarters was re-established at Burlington House, there to stay throughout the war undeterred by bombs or fire.

In 1945, after the war's end, Sir Henry spoke prophetically of some of the post-war problems which he two years later as head of the British Association was to emphasize. There was need, for example, to organize for peace-time uses the wartime developments in flying, in photography, in voyages, as well as to follow up clues hinted at in the study of blood. Perhaps through the United Nations, "a world community in science" would arise, as indeed it must if civilization is to survive. Wartime secrecy and political barriers must no longer prevent the return of the free and frank interchange of scientific ideas which had characterized the period before 1914. In those days science was truly indivisible and knew no national boundaries.

Was Sir Henry thinking as he spoke of what the Royal Society itself had already done in a notable instance to further such cooperation? In 1934 the eminent Russian physicist, Dr. Peter Kapitza, could not return from a scientific congress in the USSR to continue with his research professorship and his work as director of the Royal Society Mond Laboratory at Cambridge. He had been working in Cambridge since 1921. His associates at the Laboratory were unwilling to undertake the experimental work he had planned and prepared for if he could do it himself. To make that possible, since he was not permitted to leave his homeland, the equipment, some of which he had designed, was sold to the Russian government for his use, along with duplicates of apparatus that could not be spared. Thus Dr. Kapitza could have in Moscow the identical equipment that had been developed for his work in Cambridge. The advancement of fundamental research by a great scientist was more important than political barriers.

In 1947, Sir Henry had less to say about "a world community" but more about the freedom necessary for fundamental research and about its greater importance over applied science and technology. Again he emphasized the value of national and international cooperation for the future of science as well as the value of science itself to help bring about such cooperation. Once more he pleaded for the release of science from all the entanglements imposed in the war years.

The Fostering of Science

How science may be fostered when actively and wisely directed may perhaps be better understood if at this point a summary is made of what has been previously indicated at various places in these pages. An adequate appraisal of the scientific work conducted by the Royal Society during the past fifty years or so is beyond the competence of the author and indeed outside the domain of this book. It may not be amiss, nonetheless, to attempt an answer to the question: "What does the Royal Society do?"

Scientific work is not done by the Society acting as a unit but by its commissions and committees, or by individuals, to whom questions are referred and problems assigned. Financial aid for living expenses as well as for apparatus may be granted, and help given in publishing the results secured. Advice and criticism are available either through private consultation with the eminent specialists who are the Fellows today, or through public discussion of papers presented in the conferences which the various sectional committees organize. The usefulness of these papers is further increased by their publication in the Society's journals.

Since the Society is concerned with the whole realm of "natural" knowledge and not with one section of it, as, for example, with astronomy alone or medical science, it acts as a spokesman and a rallying center for the various scientific organizations in national and in international connections. Also, through the research funds placed at its disposal especially in recent years, it is able to sponsor and direct scientific undertakings on a broader scale than would otherwise be possible. Thus, it has administered for the government grants-in-aid for the publication of scientific papers that had accumulated in the hands of various societies during the years of the first World War. It has undertaken at government request investigation of volcanic phenomena in the West Indies and particularly on the island of Montserrat in the Leeward group. At the desire of the Colonial Office, long-continued studies in various parts of the Empire have been made of malaria, of sleeping-sickness, of Malta fever and of the causes of cattle disease. Other medical research has been done in North China, in British Guiana and in Assam. An anonymous fund for medical research received in 1924-25 made most of these expeditions possible. Indeed, the income from this fund for five years was devoted to the study of malaria both in India and in England.

Since 1923 the Society has maintained from one to seven research professorships for men whose work has proved outstanding. For example, among these research professors are Dr. Archibald V. Hill, winner of the Nobel prize in 1922 in physiology and medicine, Sir Geoffrey I. Taylor, expert in meteorology, aeronautics, mathematics and engineering, who won the Royal Medal in 1933 and the Copley Medal in 1944, and Sir Owen W. Richardson, the physicist who won a Nobel award in 1928 and a Royal Medal two years later. Similarly, the fellowships and "studentships" the Society grants have enabled such men as Lancelot Hogben, Regius Professor of Natural History (1937-41) at the University of Aberdeen, to lay the foundations for their later achievements. The number of these fellows and students has greatly increased since 1919 as the funds entrusted to the Society have grown. Such opportunities for individuals of exceptional promise mean much in later years through their teaching as well as through their own distinguished accomplishments.

In addition to freeing the individual scientist financially to develop some promising idea, the Society has also provided the place and the equipment for such study. It was a leader in establishing at Bushey House the laboratory that later became the National Physics Laboratory. It brought both the man and the equipment together when it built and equipped at Cambridge the Royal Society Mond Laboratory to further the experiments of Dr. Kapitza, already one of its research professors. Thus it aided his work in intense magnetic fields and at the same time provided an up-to-date laboratory for the study of magnetic and other effects at the lowest possible temperatures. The university provided the site and the running expenses. The Laboratory was opened in 1933 with the name Mond in memory of the Fellow whose bequest to the Society had financed the project. In this way the Society hoped to further fundamental research with the minimum of bureaucratic controls and the maximum of freedom for the investigator.

Throughout these years the Society has regularly issued the *Philosophical Transactions* and the two series of its *Proceedings*. Its occasional publications have ranged from various catalogs and its own *Record* to reports by its commissions and committees on subjects as diverse as grain pests and Antarctic expeditions. It has published monographs like the one on horny sponges and it has issued *The Scientific Work of the late Spencer Pickering, F.R.S.* (1927).

A Fellow after the first World War recorded that the services of the Society to the government were very great during those years. It is safe to assume that similar and even greater service was rendered during the second War. For in the interim between the two Wars, relations between the Society and the government had been steadily growing closer as the Society gained in strength and as it developed its main function, the furtherance of science. In this age such interdependence seems inevitable. The Society's position outside party politics would seem to be one of its sources of strength in its dealings with governmental agencies. For always, be it noted, the Society continues as an independent, private organization with its housing alone provided by the state in recognition of its public usefulness.

Three Hundred Years

The Royal Society may well be proud of its long history. During the centuries it has grown from an assembly of important men interested in the study of nature in all its aspects—amateurs of science—into an organization of distinguished scientists preeminent in their respective fields. That growth was not steady. Indeed, in the critical years toward the close of the seventeenth century, in the trivialities of the mid-eighteenth and in the stagnation of the early nineteenth, there was question whether the Society would rise above its difficulties. Finances were an ever-present problem; but even more serious was the nonscientific character of its membership. Until the scientists gained control of its administration in the nineteenth century and made election to membership selective and a privilege hard to achieve, the Society could not devote itself with full vigor to its central purpose, the advancement of natural knowledge.

The ways by which this purpose have been furthered have been many and varied. Some, like the encouragement of scientific publications, date back to its earliest days, as does also the study by its committees of questions propounded by the sovereigns or the government. Indeed, more and more during and since the latter part of the nineteenth century the Society has become the channel of communication between the government and the leading men in the different fields of scientific work. Periods of war have served to widen and strengthen the Society's usefulness in this respect. As a private organization it can make its suggestions and recommendations without publicity and without interference from red tape. For the same reasons those receiving them can do so without loss of official dignity. And the government is benefited by access to the best advice available on matters requiring specialized scientific knowledge.

Specifically, the Society has made proposals for institutions, expeditions and explorations needing government support, from the establishment of the Royal Observatory to that of the National Physical Laboratory, from geodetic surveys to Captain Cook's voyages and those undertaken by explorers in the nineteenth and twentieth centuries. Recently, it has subsidized individual students and professors and has granted funds for the tools of research and for the detailed study of important problems. It has fostered the growth of related but independent organizations and has stimulated national and international cooperation through its own activities on the *Catalogue* and through delegates as well as advice. It has rewarded achievement by medals and by money, whether that achievement were by its own Fellows, by outsiders or by foreigners. It has welcomed foreigners to its fellowship and has maintained its correspondence with scientists abroad from the earliest days. It has, in recent years especially, extended its efforts to develop and strengthen international cooperation and friendship among the workers in science everywhere. This international cross-fertilization of scientific ideas which the Society has always fostered is now being increasingly recognized as scholars study the files of its correspondence accumulated for centuries.

All this it has done as a private organization under Royal Charter, paying its own expenses as best it could until the end of the eighteenth century. Since then it has been housed by the government, but it still is privately supported. The thousands of pounds it has disbursed since 1850 for the furtherance of scientific research have come from funds entrusted to it for that purpose both by the government and by individuals,—substantial evidence of its present high position.

The Society's contributions of its collections and of the Arundel Library to the British Museum were major aids to that institution's growth, and as trustees of the Museum the Society's presidents have served now for two hundred years. Its Fellows, whether in their capacity as officers of the Society or as its representatives, have served on governing boards of institutions from schools to laboratories and observatories. And scholars from far and near have found its library a mine of treasure.

Evidence of the Society's high standing also lies in the recognition won by its officers. Sir Henry Dale's immediate predecessor in office was Sir William Bragg, Nobel prize-winner in physics. Sir Henry himself was elected head of the British Association after the close of World War II had released him from the presidency he had held throughout those years. The present incumbent is Sir Robert Robinson, recipient of the Nobel award in 1947 for his work in organic chemistry,—a worthy successor to that other chemist-president, Sir Humphry Davy, more than a hundred years ago. Such men, like the others who have been elected P.R.S. since the reform of the Society went into full effect, are in their own scientific distinction representative of the leadership now characteristic of the Society's membership.

The Future

In a few years more the Royal Society will have attained its three hundredth anniversary. No man can foresee the state of the world in 1962. Science and invention have so shrunk the distances on this earth while expanding the universe, and have so speeded up time itself that where, some hundred and more years ago, a battle was fought and won in complete ignorance that the treaty of peace ending the war was about to be signed, now listeners have heard described on the opposite side of the globe the surrender of the enemy as the formalities proceeded. Although time and space have been telescoped and marvels hardly dreamed of a century or two ago have been made daily commonplaces, man himself with his emotions, his prejudices, his superstitions even, has not kept pace with these advances. Here lies the enigma of the future.

Here also is the great opportunity for the Royal Society and its kindred associations, not alone in Britain but in all lands. As they extend the boundaries of knowledge and its uses, they are becoming more and more aware that they must have a responsible share in man's education and self-knowledge so that he may use wisely the powers science has placed in his hands. "The truth shall make you free"; but how shall man use this freedom?

From its origins in the seventeenth century to the present day, the Royal Society has attracted many of the best trained and ablest minds among the leaders of the world of which it has been a part. The Society has grown through a precocious infancy and a weak and uncertain adolescence. Then in the early nineteenth century it gathered its forces together, sharpened its purposes and during the century following, grew into the full vigor of its maturing powers. The amateurs of the early days have become the leading scientists of today. With this transformation have come increased respect for and trust in the Fellows, and also the funds necessary for their work. Their leadership is recognized, their advice sought. Already as a Society they have accomplished much. Their responsibility and their opportunity in the years to come are great.

BIBLIOGRAPHY
AND
SOURCES

This book is based primarily on the following:

A. MAJOR REFERENCES

The Record of the Royal Society (4th edit., London, 1940). This official publication includes an historical summary, chronological lists of officers, Fellows, medallists, publications, benefactions, recipients of grants, etc., as well as an alphabetical list of Fellows and tables of membership averages.   (Quoted as *Record*)

Lyons, H. *The Royal Society, 1660-1940, a History of its Administration under its Charters* (Cambridge, 1944). Important especially for financial history. A Fellow since 1906, Sir Henry Lyons was treasurer of the Society for ten years preceding World War II.
(Quoted as Lyons)

Weld, C. R. *A History of the Royal Society* (2 vols., London, 1848). Of great value especially for the years immediately preceding 1830 when it ends. Weld was assistant secretary and librarian of the Society for eighteen years. He has included many documents and much anecdotal material, carefully checked. Lists and tables in the appendices.   (Quoted as Weld)

B. MAJOR SOURCES

Birch, T. *The History of the Royal Society* (4 vols., London, 1746). A transcription of the minutes of the Society and its Council from the first days through December, 1687. All references to the minutes are to these volumes.

(Quoted as Birch)

Sprat, T. *The History of the Royal Society* (2nd edit., London, 1702). First published in 1667, this is the official account of the Society's first few years, of its philosophy and the arguments for and against it.

(Quoted as Sprat)

GENERAL REFERENCES

The Dictionary of National Biography

The Dictionary of American Biography

Taylor, F. S., *The March of Mind, A Short History of Science* (New York, 1939).

Chapter 1

Johnson, F. R. and Larkey, S. V., Thomas Digges, the Copernican system, and the idea of the infinity of the universe in 1576. *Huntington Library Bulletin,* No. 5 (April, 1934), 69-117.

Chapter 2

SOURCES

Advice of W. P[etty] to Mr. Samuel Hartlib for the Advancement of some Particular Parts of Learning (London, 1648) in *Harleian Miscellany* (London, 1810), vol. VI, 1-14.

Bacon, F. *New Atlantis* in *Works of Francis Bacon,* edit. by J. Spedding, R. L. Ellis, and D. D. Heath (Boston, n.d.), vol. V, 398-413.

Boyle, R. *Works,* edit. by T. Birch (5 vols., London, 1744), V, 258, 263, 397-399.

Cowley, A. *A Proposition for the Advancement of Experimental Philosophy* (London, 1661), preface, conclusion.

Gilbert, H. Queene Elizabethes achademy. *Early English Text Society,* edit. by F. J. Furnivall, extra series, no. viii (London, 1869), 1-12.

AUTHORITIES

Bellot, H., John Evelyn, 1620–1706. *Contemporary Review,* vol. 114 (August, 1918), 201-207.

Dircks, H. *A Biographical Memoir of Samuel Hartlib, Milton's Familiar Friend* (London, 1865), 16-19, 52.

Fulton, J. F., The rise of the experimental method; Bacon and the Royal Society of London. *Yale Journal of Biology and Medicine* (March, 1931), 308.

Houghton, W. E., The history of trades: its relation to seventeenth-century thought. *Journal of the History of Ideas,* vol. II, no. 1 (January, 1941), 41-48.

Keynes, G., John Evelyn as a bibliophil. *Library,* ser. 4, vol. XII (September, 1931), 175-199.

Masson, D. *Life of Milton* (London, 1873), vol. III, 193-231.

Spedding, J. *Life and Times of Francis Bacon* (Boston, 1878), vol. II, 619-620.

Stimson, D., Hartlib, Haak and Oldenburg, Intelligencers. *Isis,* no. 84, vol. XXXI, 2 (April, 1940), 309-326.

For discussion of Comenius' visit to England: Young, R. F. *Comenius in England* . . . (Oxford, 1932); Stimson, D., Comenius and the 'invisible college,' *Isis,* no. 66, vol. XXIII, 2 (September, 1935), 377-388; A. C. S., Notes on the foundation and history of the Royal Society. *Notes and Records of the Royal Society,* No. 1 (April, 1938), 32-36; and *supra,* footnote, p. 37.

Chapter 3

SOURCES

Aubrey, J. *Brief Lives* . . . edit. by A. Clark (2 vols., Oxford, 1898), I, 300; II, 299.

Wallis, J. *Defence of the Royal Society* (London, 1678).

"Dr. Wallis's account of some passages of his own life," January 29, 1696/7, *Works of Thomas Hearne* (London, 1810), vol. III, cxl-clxiv. (These two accounts are combined in the *Record,* 4-6.)

Ward, John. *Lives of the Professors of Gresham College* (London, 1740).

Wilkins, J. *Of the Principles and Duties of Natural Religion* (London, 1693), 80.

———. *Mathematical Magick* (2nd ed., London, 1680), Bk. 2, chapters 2, 4, 5.

AUTHORITIES

Allen, P., Medical education in 17th century England. *Jour. of the Hist. of Med. and Allied Sci.,* vol. I, no. 1 (January, 1946), 115-143.

Houghton, W. E., The English virtuoso in the seventeenth century. *Jour. of the Hist. of Ideas,* vol. III, nos. 1 and 2 (January and April, 1942), 51-73, 190-219.

———. Gresham College; precursor of the Royal Society. *Jour. of the Hist. of Ideas,* vol. I, no. 4 (October, 1940), 413-438.

Stimson, D., Puritanism and the "new philosophy," in 17th century England. *Bull. of the Institute of the Hist. of Med.,* vol. III, no. 5 (May, 1935), 321-334.

On Puritanism and science, see also, Merton, R. K., Science, technology and society in 17th century England. *Osiris,* vol. IV, pt. 2 (1938), and Jones, R. F. *Ancients and Moderns* (St. Louis, 1936).

Chapter 4

SOURCES

"Ballad of Gresham Colledge," British Museum: Add. MS. 34,217, fos. 30*v*-31*r*; Sloane MS. 1,326, fos. 116-120*v* and 363, fos. 38-41. See also Stimson, D. 'Ballad of Gresham Colledge.' *Isis,* vol. XVIII, 1, no. 52 (July, 1932), 103-117; and *supra,* p. 65, note 3.

Boyle, R. *Works,* ed. by T. Birch (5 vols., London, 1744), I, 5, 20; V, 320, 334, 364, 375, 392.

Evelyn, J. *Diary and Correspondence,* ed. by W. Bray (London, 1818).

Pepys, S. *Diary,* ed. by H. B. Wheatley (9 vols., London, 1926).

The Philosophical Society, ed. by R. T. Gunther. Early Science in Oxford, vol. IV (London, 1925).

Pope, W. *Life of . . . Seth, Lord Bishop of Salisbury* (London, 1697), 27.

Wren, *Parentalia* (London, 1750), 247, 254.

BIBLIOGRAPHY AND SOURCES

AUTHORITIES

Browne, C. A., Scientific notes from the books and letters of John Winthrop, Jr. (1606-1676). *Isis*, no. 36, vol. XI (December, 1928), 325-346.

D'Israeli, I. *Calamities and Quarrels of Authors* (2 vols., London, n.d.), II, 341 n.

Stimson, D., Hartlib, Haak and Oldenburg: Intelligencers. *Isis*, no. 84, vol. XXXI, 2 (April, 1940), 309-326.

———. Dr. Wilkins and the Royal Society. *Jour. of Mod. Hist.*, vol. III, no. 4 (December, 1931), 539-563.

Wells, J. *Oxford and its Colleges* (12th ed., London, 1923), 262.

For the story of the mace, see Weld, I, 152-165.

Chapter 5

SOURCES

Behn, A. *Works*, ed. by M. Summers (London, 1915), III, 388, 390-497.

Butler, S. *Genuine Remains in Verse and Prose* (London, 1759), 1-56.

Glanvill, J. *Vanity of Dogmatizing* (London, 1661).

J. G. [Joseph Glanvill], *A further Discovery of Mr. Stubbe in a Brief Reply to his last pamphlet against Jos. Glanvill* (London, 1671), 27-28.

Neal, D. *History of the Puritans*, ed. by Toulmin (London, 1822), III, 393n.

Royal Society MSS., *Classified Papers*, IV (1), no. 17; also transcribed in Birch, I, 36.

Shadwell, T. *Works* (London, 1720), I, 341, 344 ff.

Sorbière, S. *Relation d'un Voyage en Angleterre où sont touchés plusieurs choses, qui regardent l'estat des sciences et de la religion, et autres matières curieuses* (Paris, 1664), 79-92.

Sprat, T. *Observations on Mons. de Sorbière's Voyage into England* (London, 1665), 235, 237, 242.

Stubbe, H. *Campanella Revised, or an Enquiry into the History of the Royal Society* (London, 1670). "To the Reader."

———. *The Plus Ultra Reduced to a Non Plus* . . . (London, 1670), 40-41, 153.

Wood, A. *Athenae Oxoniensis,* ed. by P. Bliss (London, 1817), III, 1067, 1070-1071.

Wotton, W. *Reflections upon Ancient and Modern Learning* (2nd ed., London, 1697), 419.

AUTHORITIES

Lloyd, C., Shadwell and the virtuosi. *Pub. Mod. Lang Assoc.,* vol. XLIV (December, 1930), 472n, 494.

MacCarthy, B. G. *Women Writers, Their Contribution to the English Novel, 1621-1744* (Cork University, 1944), 81-82, 91, 120.

Mussr, R. and Krantz, J. C., Jr., The friendship of Robert Boyle and Christopher Wren. *Bull. of the Hist. of Medicine,* VIII, no. 8 (October, 1939), 972-973.

Pearson, N., The virtuosi. *Nineteenth Century,* vol. LXVI (November, 1909), 859.

Sonnichsen, C. L. *The Life and Works of Thomas Sprat* (1931), an unpublished dissertation, Harvard University. The author graciously lent his copy to the writer.

Stimson, D., Christopher Wren, F. R. S. *Scientific Monthly,* vol. LIII (October, 1941), 360-367.

Chapter 6

SOURCES

Grew, N. *Musaeum Regalis Societatis* (London, 1681), 388.

Royal Society MSS. "Miscell.: Papers of Councils, Committees, etc."

Sources listed under chapters 4 and 5.

AUTHORITIES

Armitage, A., Our first Astronomer Royal . . . *Science Progress* no. 135 (July 1946), 506-515.

Gosse, E. *History of Eighteenth Century Literature, 1660-1780* (London, 1889), 75-76.

More, L. T. *Isaac Newton, a Biography*. (New York, 1934), 154, 156, 252, 510-518.

Stimson, D., Dr. Wilkins and the Royal Society. *Jour. of Mod. Hist.* III, no. 4 (December, 1931), 562-3n.

Wheatley, H. B. *The Early History of the Royal Society*. The Sette of Odde Volumes, No. 35 (London, 1905).

Chapter 7

SOURCES

The Spectator, ed. by G. A. Aitken (6 vols., London, n.d.) vol. I.

The Tatler, ed. by G. A. Aitken (4 vols., n.p., n.d.)

Swift, J. *Gulliver's Travels,* ed. by T. Scott, in Swift's *Prose Works,* vol. III.

Ward, J. *Lives of the Professors of Gresham College* (London, 1740), 18.

AUTHORITIES

Craig, J. *Newton at the Mint* (Cambridge, 1946).

More, L. T. *Isaac Newton, a Biography* (New York, 1934).

Whiteley, J. H. *Wesley's England: A Survey of Eighteenth Century Social and Cultural Conditions* (London, 1945).

On *Gulliver's Travels:* Nicolson, M. and Mohler, N., Scientific background of Swift's 'Voyage to Laputa.' *Annals of Science,* II, no. 3 (July, 1937), 301-334; Gould, S. J., Gulliver and the moons of Mars. *Jour. of the Hist. of Ideas,* VI (January, 1945), 91; Case, A. E. *Four Essays on Gulliver's Travels* (Princeton, 1945), 89-91.

On the later history of Gresham College: *An Encyclopedia of London* (New York, c. 1937), 353; *London and its Environs* ed. by Muirhead, Findlay and Muirhead (4th ed. London, 1935) 260; "Sir Thomas Gresham," *Encyclopedia Britannica,* 11th edit.

Chapter 8

SOURCES

Hill, J. *A Review of the Works of the Royal Society* . . . (London, 1751).

Wren. *Parentalia* (London, 1750).

Young, E. *Poetical Works,* edit. by J. Mitford (Boston, n.d.).

AUTHORITIES

Bonno, G., Hans Sloane et les relations intellectuelles Franco-Anglaises au dix-huitième siècle (d'après des documents inédits). *Romanic Review* XXXIV, no. 1 (February, 1943), 40-49.

D'Israeli, I. *Calamities and Quarrels of Authors,* ed. by his son (2 vols. London, n.d.) II, 364-374 and notes.

Emery, C., 'Sir' John Hill versus the Royal Society. *Isis,* vol. XXXIV (summer, 1942) 16-20.

Chapter 9

For this summary of the election procedures and for the election of colonial Fellows, full use has been made of the carefully documented article by Raymond P. Stearns, "Colonial Fellows of the Royal Society of London, 1661-1788," *The William and Mary Quarterly,* 3rd Series, vol. III, no. 2 (April, 1946), 208-268.

On American Fellows, see Heindel, R. Heathcote, Americans and the Royal Society, 1783-1937. *Science,* n.s. 87 (March 25, 1938), 267-272.

Both articles have been supplemented by Weld's *History* as far as it goes, by the *Record,* Lyons, and articles in the *Dictionary of National Biography* and the *Dictionary of American Biography.*

Silliman's and Dana's claims to scientific eminence are based on the biography by Fulton, J. F. and Thomson, E. H. *Benjamin Silliman, Pathfinder in American Science* (New York, 1947), 54-56, 243-247.

See also Tredinnick, F. A., Jr. *Cotton Mather, Puritan Scientist, A Study of his Curiosa Americana.* Unpublished M. A. thesis, Columbia University, June, 1947. The *Curiosa* are Mather's letters to the Royal Society.

Chapter 10

SOURCE

Granville, A. B. *The Royal Society in the Nineteenth Century* (London, 1836).

BIBLIOGRAPHY AND SOURCES

AUTHORITIES

Dale, H., The Royal Society and its Homes. *Nature,* vol. 152 (December 4, 1943), 649.

Fulton, J. F., The Warrington Academy (1757-1786) and its influence upon medicine and science. *Bull. of the Hist. of Med.* vol. I, no. 2 (February, 1933), 54-56, 59.

Garrison, F. H., Medicine in the *Tatler, Spectator* and *Guardian. Bull. of the Hist. of Med.* vol. II (October, 1934), 501.

Geikie, A. *Annals of the Royal Society Club* (London, 1917).

Parker, I. *Dissenting Academies in England* (Cambridge, 1914), 46-122.

Turner, D. M. *History of Science Teaching in England* (London, 1927), 40-86.

Whiteley, J. H. *Wesley's England* (London, 1945), 33, 43, 44.
For the story about Franklin's lightning rods, see Weld, II, 93-103.

Chapter 11

SOURCES

An Authentic Account of the Dissensions and Debates in the Royal Society (London, 1784).

Babbage, C. *Reflections on the Decline of Science in England and on Some of its Causes.* (London, 1830.)

Barrow, Sir J. *Sketches of the Royal Society and the Royal Society Club.* (London, 1849), 10, 33, 36, 40.

Granville, A. B. *The Royal Society in the Nineteenth Century* (London, 1836).

"Peter Pindar" [John Wolcot], *Peter's Prophecy; or, the President and Poet; or, an Important Epistle to Sir Jos. Banks, on the Approaching Election of a President of the Royal Society.* (Dublin, 1789.)

AUTHORITIES

Bragg, W., History in the archives of the Royal Society. *Science,* n.s. 89 (May 19, 1939), 445-453.

Geikie, A. *Annals of the Royal Society Club* (London, 1917).

Turner, D. M., *History of Science Teaching in England* (London, 1927).

Woodward, E. L. *The Age of Reform, 1815-70.* (Oxford History of England, 1938), 471-473, 490.

Chapter 12

SOURCES

Anon. *Sir Joseph Banks and the Royal Society: A Popular Biography with an Historical Introduction and Sequel.* (London, 1844.)

Babbage, C. *The Ninth Bridgewater Treatise, A Fragment* (Philadelphia, 1841).

Barrow, Sir J. *Sketches of the Royal Society and the Royal Society Club.* (London, 1849), 51, 88, 92, 94, 106-7.

[Gosse, E.] *Father and Son, Biographical Recollections* (New York, 1907), chapter 5.

Granville, A. B. *The Royal Society in the Nineteenth Century* (London, 1836).

Hooker, J. D. *Address of the President delivered at the Anniversary Meeting of the Royal Society* (London, 1875), 6.

AUTHORITIES

Bonney, T. G. *Annals of the Philosophical Club of the Royal Society* (London, 1919).

Bragg, W., History in the archives of the Royal Society. *Science,* n.s. 89 (May 19, 1939), 449.

Geikie, A. *Annals of the Royal Society Club* (London, 1917).

Todhunter, I. *William Whewell, Master of Trinity College, Cambridge: An Account of his Writings with Selections from his Literary and Scientific Correspondence* (2 vols. London, 1876), II, 129, 135.

Turner, D. M. *History of Science Teaching in England* (London, 1927).

Woodward, E. L. *The Age of Reform, 1815-70.* (Oxford History of England, 1938.)

Chapter 13

The facts and figures in this chapter have been taken mainly from the lists of benefactions, of recipients of awards and similar evidence in the *Record,* supplemented by the treasurer's intimate knowledge of the Society's affairs during the nearly forty years of his membership in the Society as given in Lyons.

Bragg, W., Presidential address, Nov. 30, 1937. *Proceedings of the Royal Society,* Series B. vol. 124, pp. 383-4.

—— History in the archives of the Royal Society. (Pilgrim Trust Lecture, April 24, 1939.) *Science,* n.s. vol. 89 (May 19, 1939), 445-453.

Dale, H., The Royal Society and its homes. *Nature,* vol. 152 (Dec. 4, 1943), 649-651.

The Pilgrim Trust Lecture. *Nature,* vol. 142 (December 17, 1938), p. 1068.

Chapter 14

For this chapter the *Record* and Lyons have been supplemented by personal observation (July, 1939) and by the following:

Bonney, T. G. *Annals of the Philosophical Club of the Royal Society* (London, 1919), 27ff., 95.

Dale, H., Address at the Anniversary Meeting of the Royal Society, Nov. 30, 1945, *Proceedings of the Royal Society,* Series B. vol. 133 (Feb. 12, 1946), 123-139.

—— The Royal Society and its homes, *Nature,* vol. 152 (December 4, 1943), 649-651.

Election of Statesmen as Fellows of the Royal Society. *Science,* n.s. vol. 71 (June 27, 1930), 656.

Lists of Candidates: *Science,* n.s. vol. 101 (April 13, 1945) 372-373; *Nature,* vol. 157 (March 23, 1946), 363; vol. 159 (March 29, 1947), 429.

(Princess Elizabeth), *Baltimore Sun,* July 4, 1947.

(Waldemar Kaempffert's report on the 1947 meeting of the British Association) *New York Times,* August 28, 1947.

For Dr. Kapitza, see Sir Ernest Rutherford, Address at the Anniversary Meeting of the Royal Society, Dec. 1, 1930, *Proceedings of the*

Royal Society, Series A, no. 813 (January 1, 1931), 249-254; Sir F. Gowland Hopkins, Address at the Anniversary meeting . . . Nov. 30, 1935, *Proceedings of the Royal Society*, Series A, no. 879 (January 1, 1936), 258; *Nature*, vol. 135 (May 4, 1935), 755, and vol. 136 (November 23, 1935), 825.

INDEX

Académie des Sciences, 64, 175
Academies, dissenting, 166-8, 180
Acton lands 136-7, 230
Addison, Joseph, 127-30, 163, 181
Advancement of Learning, 12, 14
Aggassiz, Louis, 158
Agriculture, 15, 106, 131, 175, 178
Amateurs (science-lovers), 27; organized, 30, 44-5; foreign, 32; activities, 23 *et seq.*, 96, 246; personnel, 34, 56, 148, 198; importance, 36, 115, 218-19, 249-50; influence on style, 108-11;. proportion to scientists, 137, 157, 237-8; *see also* Virtuosi
American Academy of Arts and Sciences, Boston, 156
American Association for the Advancement of Science, 191
American Philosophical Society, 157
Anderson, John, 182; Anderson's Institution, 182
Anne, Queen, 52, 113, 118, 120, 134
Antiquarians, 117, 140; Society of, 140, 176
"Atlantis," 15, 16
Arber, Agnes, 238
Aristotle, 1 *et seq.*, 40, **75-6**
Arundel House, 47, 103
Asquith, Henry H., 237
Association of American Geologists and Naturalists 191,
Astronomy: workers in, 29, 111-14, 137, 180, 188; theories and observations, 37-8, 40-1, 43, 74, 202 *et seq.;* Winthrop, 55-6; satires on, 58, 94, 127, 132; organizations, 185, 233, 241; *see also* Telescopes
Aubrey, John, 41, 63-4
Audubon, James, 158

Babbage, Charles, 186, 190-5, 210
Bache, Alexander, 158-9
Bacon, Francis, 2, 10-14 *et seq.*, 36, 42, 60, 71, 75, 88, 207
Baldwin, Stanley, 237
Ball, William, 102
Ballad of Gresham College, 56-63, 138
Banks, Joseph, 116-17, 140, 157 *et seq.*, 172; explorations, 173-4, 189; Iceland, 174; patron of science, 176; P.R.S., 177-8, 209; attitude to scientific societies, 183, 207; autocratic rule, 186-90, 194; criticism of, 189-90, 205, 214
Barometer, 42, 44, 80, 90, 91, 127, 138
Barrow, Isaac, 54, 167
Barrow, James, 185, 190, 204
"Battle of the books," 76, 95
Beaumont, William, 159
Behn, Mrs. Aphra, 91, 94, **95**
Birch, Thomas, 140, 167
Bohr, Niels, 139
Botany and biology: medical botany, 10, **32,** 40, 155; gardens, 19-20, 62; classification, 111; collections,

133-4, 145, 154, 176, 178; satires on, 128-31, 142; popular interest in, 181; organizations, 183, 224, 241; *see also* Microscope

Bowditch, Nathaniel, 158, 159

Bowdoin, James, 156, 158

Boyle, Robert: friends of, 15-16, 20-1, 77, 131; "invisible college," 37 *and* 37*n*, 38-9, 52, 54; work, 43-4, 55, 59, 80 *et seq.;* at Oxford, 47-8, 76, 88; and Oldenburg, 65 *et seq.,* 73, 90; refused presidency, 98-9; death, 126; notes scarcity of scientists, 197; and theology, 204

Boylston, Zabdiel, 153-4

Bragg, William, 139, 184, 198; P.R.S., 234-5, 248

Battle, Thomas, 153; William, 153

Bridgewater, Earl of, 204

Bridgewater Treatises, 204-5, 215

Briggs, Henry, 29, 167

British Academy, 232

British Association for the Advancement of Science, 185, 218, 239, 248; formation, 191; preamble of constitution, 195-6; relations with Royal Society, 223, 228, 230

British Museum, 103, 135, 177-8, 209, 248

Brouncker, Lord, 78; first P.R.S., 13, 101

Bruno, Giordano, 2

Buffon, Georges, Comte de, 125, 136

Burlington House, 228, 241, 242

Burnet, William, 153

Butler, Samuel, 91-2, 127

Byrd, William, 152-3

Calendar, reform of, 169

Cambridge University, 9, 28, 29, 39, 54, 58, 97, 113, 120, 167, 180-1, 201-2, 229, 243

Carbery, John, Earl of, 99-101

Catalogue of Scientific Papers, 227, 230-1, 247

Cavendish, Henry, 203

Cavendish Laboratories, Cambridge, 202

Charles II, 50, 73, 121, 201; Founder and Patron, 6, 47, 52 *et seq.,* 64,

121, 185; scientific interests, 32, 80-1, 111-12; virtuoso, 36; anecdotes, 53, 80; visit to Royal Society, 78-9; Chelsea College gift, 104; portrait, 222

Chelsea College, 65, 104

Chemistry: interest in, 16, 32, 54, 55, 74; satirized, 92; professors of, 159, 180-1, 184; leaders in, 195, 203, 205-9, 237, 248; organizations, 224, 233, 241

Churchill, Winston, 237

Clocks and watches, 43, 44, 138, 174-5

Colbert, 64

Colchester, Lord, 210

Collections, *see* Royal Society: Activities; Museums; British Museum

Comenius, Amos, 14, 15, 18

Cook, James, 139, 173-4, 201, 247

Copernicus, Nicholas, 1, 4, 10, 38, 40-1, 43

Copley Medal, 138-9, 156, 170, 176, 193, 225

Council of Royal Society, 54, 78, 83, 104, 123, 187, 210, 221; powers of, 148-9, 177, 192-3, 216, 239; scientist members, 147-9, 205

Cowley, Abraham, 18, 21-3, 71; *Ode to the Royal Society,* 21

Crane Court House, 121-5, 127, 131, 176-7

Cromwell, Oliver, 19, 39, 45, 53; Richard, 50; Robina, wife of John Wilkins, 50

Dale, Henry, P.R.S., 238-9, 241-2, 248

Dalton, John, 195, 203, 208

Dana, James Dwight, 159

Darwin, Charles, 180; Erasmus, 180

Davy, Humphry, 162, 184, 190, 195; P.R.S., 181, 206-9, 248

Davy Medal, 207, 226

De Fabrica Humani Corporis, 41

De Revolutionibus, 41

Descartes, René, 35, 42, 44

Description of the Famous Kingdom of Macaria, 15

Diderot, Denis, 163

Digby, Kenelm, 32, 61

INDEX

Digges, Leonard, 2; Thomas, 2
Disraeli, Benjamin, 237
D'Israeli, Isaac, 143-4
Dissenters, 165-7
Dryden, John, 100
Dudley, Paul, 153

Education: criticism of, 9, 23-4; for youths, 27, adults, 27-30, 124, workers, 181-2, 183-4; medical, 10, 28; plans for: Gilbert's, 9-10, Comenius', 14, Hartlib's, 15, Petty's, 17, Cowley's, 21-3; science in, 165-8, 182, 202; share of Royal Society in, 228-9, 248
Einstein, Albert, 139
"Elephant in the Moon," 91
Elizabeth, Princess, 237-8
"Emperor in the Moon," 94
England, conditions in time of: Elizabeth, 1-2, 31; early Stuarts, 3-4, 30-1; Cromwell, 3, 45; William and Mary, 100-1, Hanoverians, 118-20, 161-4, 200-1, 218; Victoria, 161, 223; see also Industrial Revolution
English style 75, 108-11
Ent, George, 37, 38, 54, 78
Europe, conditions in: 17th century, 31-2, 118-19; 18th century, 162-3, 165; 19th century, 200
Evelyn, John: designed frontispiece. 13; activities, 18-21, 51, 61, 80, 98; proposed society, 20-1; at Wadham College, 49; at Oxford, 77; named Royal Society, 52; suggested motto, 64; visited Oldenburg, 67; scorned critics, 89; recorded Ball's gift, 102; secured Arundel Library, 103; suggested English studies, 109-10; death, 126; *Diary*, 19; *Fumifugium*, 62; *Sylva*, 107

Faraday, Michael, 184, 195, 203
Fellows of Royal Society: Original or Charter, 54 *et seq.*, 98, 152, 241; "gentlemen," 56, 115, 139-40, 212-13; American colonial, 55, 99, 125, 149, 151-7; Americans as foreigners, 158-60; foreign members, 114, 125, 132, 136, 148, 156-8, 160, 209; limitation of numbers, 98, 198, 209-10, 237-9; election procedures, 148-51, 216-17; criticisms of, 188-9, 194, 212-13; qualifications, 191-2, 209, 236-8; participation, 221, 239; women, 237-8; modern non-scientists, 237
Flamsteed, John, 43, 107, 111-13, 121, 132, 137
Foster, Samuel, 38, 47
Franklin, Benjamin, 125, 139, 155, 156; on lightning rods, 169-72, 181

Galen, Claudius, 4, 34-5
Galileo, Galilei, 5, 10, 35, 40 *et seq.*
Garden, Alexander, 155
Geodetic survey, 102, 106, 247
Geological Society, 185, 205
Geology, 159, 185, 202, 210, 233, 241, 243
George III, 172, 175-6, 199, 210
George IV, 199, 208
Gilbert, Humphrey, 9, 23, 26
Gilbert, William, 10, 42, 43, 44
"Gimcrack, Sir Nicholas," 92-94, 95, 101, 128-30
Gladstone, William, 237
Glanvill, Joseph, 57, 81, 88-9
Glisson, Francis, 55
Goddard, Jonathan, 37 *et seq.*, 79
Gosse, Edmond, 109, 205
Granville, Augustus B., 162, 185-6, 190-5, 210-14
Gray, Asa, 159
Gresham, Thomas, 26, 27, 121, 124
Gresham College, 26, 28-30 *et seq.*, 57-8, 74-5, 103, 114, 126, 167, 221; move from and later history, 121-4; confusion with Royal Society, 132
Greshamites, 30; men of Gresham, 95
Grew, Nehemiah, 65, 103, 107, 111, 131
Grove, William R., 215-16
Gulliver's Travels, 130-2

Haak, Theodore, 31-2, 38-9, 54
Hales, Stephen, 137, 139, 174

Halley, Edmond: importance as astronomer, 42, 43, 44, 132, 137, 173; and Newton, 97, 108, 113; editor, 100
Harrison, John, 138, 174, 175
Hartlib, Samuel, 14-16, 24, 31, 32, 65
Harvard University, 153, 158
Harvey, William, 4, 41, 42-4
Herschel, John F. W., 202; candidate for P.R.S., 162, 210
Herschel, William, 139, 175-6, 180, 202; Caroline, 203
Hill, John, 140-6, 169, 181, 186, 237
History of the Royal Society, 13-14, 36, 70-3 et seq., 109, 126
Hooke, Robert, 42, 44, 55, 72, 106, 131; curator, 43 et seq.; editor, 69, 107; microscopic work, 76-7, 78, 81, satirized, 92; opposition to Newton, 117, to move, 121-2; death, 117, 126
Hosack, David, 158
Howard, Charles, 61; Henry, 103
Humboldt, Alexander von, 229
Hunter, John, 139, 168; William, 168
Hutton, Charles, 187-8

Industrial Revolution, 164, 196, 197, 201
Instruments, scientific, 12, 35-6 et seq., 78, 138, 158, 164, 168, 175, 183, 197; see also Barometer; Magnet; Microscope; Telescope; Clocks and Watches; Logarithms, Tables of
Intelligencers, 15, 32, 65, 69
International Association of Academies, 231-3
International Research Council, 231-3, 235
International Unions, 232-3, 235
"Invisible College," 5, 26, 32, 37-44 et seq., 105

James II, 81, 120, 238
Jenner, Edward, 168, 181, 195
Journal des Savans, 66

Kapitza, Peter, 242-3, 245
Kepler, Johann, 42, 43, 44
Kew Gardens, 145, 176, 178; observatory in, 228
King, William, 143
King's College, London, 202

Langmuir, Irving, 234
Laplace, Pierre, 202
Lectureships, see Royal Society: Activities
Lee, Arthur, 155
Leeuwenhoek, Antonj van, 129, 221
Leibnitz, Gottfried, 44
Leverett, John, 153
Libraries, public, 182; of Royal Society, q.v.: Activities
Lightning rods, 168-72
Lind, James, 137, 174
Linné, Carl, 183
Linnean Society, 183, 185, 223, 241
Livius, Peter, 155-6
Lloyd, Claude, 93
Logarithms, Tables of, 29, 44
Lonsdale, Kathleen, 238
Lucasian professorship, Cambridge, 167
Lunar Society, Birmingham, 180
Lyell, Charles, 203
Lyons, Henry, 106, 137, 157, 227

Macclesfield, Lord, P.R.S., 168-9
Macdonald, Ramsay, 237
Magnet (loadstone), 33, 43, 49, 59, 82-3
Malpighi, Marcello, 41, 107
Manchester College, Oxford, 167
Mathematical Magick, 35
Mathematics: professors of, 29, 97, 167; problems in, 35 et seq., 63, 208; Archimedes, 48; satirized, 92, 131-2; mathematicians, number of, 137, 178, 205; Tripos, 180; Union of, 233
Mather, Cotton, 141, 150, 152-3
Maty, Paul H., 187-9
Maupertuis, Pierre L. M. de, 125, 136

Mechanics Institutes, 181-2, 195
Medicine: doctors of, 10, 37 *et seq.*, 153 *et seq.*, 168, 245; training in, 28; work in, 84-6, 137, 227, 244; satirized, 92, 129, 188, 192; numbers, 213, 236-7
Mercers Company, 27, 29, 105, 121-3
Merrit, Christopher, 37, 39
Meteorology, 12, 138, 229, 240, 245
Methodists, 120, 201
Metternich, Age of, 200
Micrographia, 76-7, 81, 92, 107
Microscope, 33-4, 43, 76-7, 82, 129, 221
Mitchell, John, 154
Montagu, Lady Mary Wortley, 137
Montesquieu, Charles de, 125, 136, 163
Moray, Robert, 52-3, 60, 63, 73-4, 97, 112
Morgan, John, 155
Morris, Robert, 154-5
Mortimer, Cromwell, 144
Moulin, Pierre, 32; Louis and Peter, 32
Museums, 20, 26-7, 33, 102; *see also* British Museum; Royal Society: Activities: collections

National Physical Laboratory, 228, 245, 247
Neile, William, 49, 54
New Atlantis, 12-14
Newcastle, Margaret, Duchess of, 82-4, 238
Newton, Isaac: pre-eminence, 6, 42, 44, 185; scientific work, 43, 107-8; activities, 97, 163; and Sloane, 103, 123, 126, 132; P.R.S., 113-17, 120-32, 138, 179; knighted, 120; death, 126
Novum Organum, 11-12, 14
Nuffield, Viscount, 237

Observations, 74-5, 103
Oldenburg, Henry: foreigner, 31; relations with Boyle, 54, 73; secretary and editor, 65-9, 102, 107, 135; in prison, 67-8, 70, 90; death, 98

Oglethorpe, James, 154
"On the Royal Society," 91-2
Opticks, 117
Organon, 12
Oxford Philosophical Society, 5, 46-8, 54, 105, 167
Oxford University, 9, 28, 29, 39, 45, 54, 58, 76-7, 113, 167-8, 201, 229

Pascal, Blaise, 42, 44
Pasteur, Louis, 203
Pavlov, Ivan, 139
Pembroke, Earl of: P.R.S., 100-1
Penn, William, 99, 152
Pepys, Samuel: diary, 67, 80; Duchess's visit, 82-3, 238; P.R.S., 98-100; death, 126
Petty, William: book, 16-18, 24; at Oxford, 46 *et seq.*; Fellow, 54, 55, 60, 64, 72, 106; knighted, 121
Philosophical Club, 217-18, 241
Philosophical Collections, see Philosophical Transactions
Philosophical Transactions: origins, 65-9; satires on, 90 *et seq.*, 131, 140-4; suspension of, 100, 107-8, 135; supervision of, 114, 144, 169; papers in, 137, 146, 171, 185, 205, 212 *et seq.*; Advertisement, 144; importance of, 146, 245
Physics: subjects, 35 *et seq.*, 169 *et seq.*, 181, 183-4, 208, 214; leaders in, 203 *et seq.*, 215-16, 237, 238, 241-2, 245, 248; organizations in, 224, 240-1; *see also* Mathematics
Pierce, Benjamin, 158, 159
Pilgrim Trust Lecture, 234-5
"Pindar, Peter," 178, 189-90, 205
Pope, Walter, 49, 54
Priestley, Joseph, 139, 166, 180, 203
Principia, 97, 107-8
Pringle, John, 172
Ptolemy, Claudius, 1, 40
Puritans, 34-5, 39, 71, 73, 165, 168

Raleigh, Walter, 4, 9
Ray, John, 107-8, 111, 133, 181
Reason, Age of, 163

Réaumur, René de, 125, 136
Reflections upon Ancient and Modern Learning, 95-6
Reforms, humanitarian, 200-2
Rélation, 73
Review of the Works of the Royal Society, 141
Rittenhouse, David, 158
Robie, Thomas, 153
Robinson, Robert: P.R.S., 248
Rockefeller, John D., 237
Rooke, Lawrence, 47, 48, 72, 221
Rousseau, Jean-Jacques, 163
Royal Astronomical Society, 113, 185, 241
Royal Institution, 159, 183-5, 207, 234
Royal Medals, 193, 199, 208, 216, 226
Royal Observatory, Greenwich, 74, 111-14, 169, 247
Royal Society:

Purpose
5-6, 89, 107, 184, 218-19, 243-7

Organization
name, 6, 52, 63; benefactor, 33; founders, 34, 40, 54; motto, 35 *and* 35n., 63, 64; charters, 52-4, 63, 76, 192, 216-17, 240; charter-book, 52, 74, 120, 199; journal book, 50-2, 97, 140, 150; Royal Patrons, 52-4, 120, 176, 199; mace, 53-4, 63, 222; date of founding, 53, 249; annual meeting, 63-4; membership, 51-2, 97-8, 101-2, 132, 137, 147-51, 188 *et seq.*, 212-13, 217, 236-8, *see also* Fellows; curators, 65; Council, *q.v.*; presidents: 100-1, 140, 168-9; powers, 193; term of office, 194, 213-14, 239; contested election, 210; distinction of, 248-9; present, 248; secretaries, 65, 68, 135-6, 143-4, 187-9, 239; treasurers, 102, 194, 211, 213, 216, 227, 239; statutes, revision of, 148-51, 209, 216, 239; finances, 64-5, 70, 101-6, 136-7, 148-9, 177, 198, 216-17, 223 *et seq.*, 248; meeting places: Gresham College, Arundel House, Crane Court House, Somerset House, Burlington House, *q.v.*; central location, 223, 241-2; committees: policy, 106, 170-1, 221, 243-4; on Papers, 69, 144, 169, 214-15; on sensitive plants, 80; on Correspondence, 106-7; "georgical," 106; on English tongue, 109-11; on Finance, 194, 221; on Charters, 216; on Library, 220; regular and special, 221; sectional, 240-1

Activities
Summarized, 243-6; methods, 25, 144, 170-1; collections, 33-4, 89-90, 102-3, 107, 114, 123, 129; Winthrop gift, 154; gift to British Museum, 177, 209, 248; visitors, 73-5, 78 *et seq.*, 125, 222; experiments, 78 *et seq.*; Library, 103, 114, 123, 137, 212, 220, 248; publications, 107-8, 114, 212, 227-8, 245-6, 247, *Philosophical Transactions, q.v., Proceedings*, 212, 245, *Record*, 245; expeditions sponsored, 159, 173-5, 227, 247; relations with government, 114, 138, 173-5, 208-9, 223-5, 244, 246-7; international relations, 229-35, 247-8; special funds: lectureships, 193, 234-5, Donation, 195, 206, 226, Scientific Relief, 225, Research, 226-7, 245, medals, 225-6, 247, government grants, 223-5, 247, other, 206, 223, 225; support of scientists, 244-5, 247; Royal Society Mond Laboratory, 243, 245
Royal Society Club, 217-18
Rumford, Count, *see* Thompson, Benjamin
Rumford Medal, 156, 193, 225

"Salomon's House," 12-13, 20, 22
Savilian professorships, Oxford, 29, 48, 167
Scarbrough (Scarburgh), Charles, 37, 39, 84
Science and theology, 203-5
Science Without a Head, 191, 210
Scientific method, 11, 13, 24, 72-3, 79, 197, 202-3
Scientists (men of science): contrasted with amateurs, *q.v.*, 36, 96, 198, 246-50; in 17th century, 55-6, 69;

in 19th century, 218-19; numbers, 96, 115, 137, 236-7, 239; American, 158-60

Shadwell, Thomas, 91, 92-4, 127, 130

Silliman, Benjamin, 159

Sloane, Hans, 101, 133, 155, 161; collections, 103, 134-5, 145, 177; P.R.S., 104, 116-17, 132, 136-8, 139, 168, 179; secretary, 114, 123, 135-6; vice-president, 126

Smallpox, 137, 162, 168

Smith, Adam, 181

Smith, James, 183

Smithsonian Institution, 159

Smuts, Jan C., 237

Society of Arts, 182

Society for the Diffusion of Useful Knowledge, 182

Soirées, 222

Somerset House, 125, 209, 222-3

Sorbière, Samuel, 73-5

South, James, 193, 210

South, Robert, 77, 89

Spectator, 127-30

Sprat, Thomas, 48, 54, 70-6; History, 13, 18, 36, 56, 88, 206; influence of Cowley, 21, 71; and Sorbière, 73-5; satirists, 81, 90-1; style, 109, 126

Steele, Richard, 127-8, 14c, 163, 181, 237

Stephenson, Marjorie, 238

Stubbs, Henry, 81, 86-9, 95, 105

Sussex, Royal Duke of, P.R.S., 162, 210-15, 229

Swift, Jonathan, 126, 130-2, 143

Sydenham, Thomas, 88 and 88n

Syllogistic reasoning, 11, 71

Tatler, 127, 141

Telescope, 2, 32, 38, 40, 56, 58, 90, 91, 138, 176

Tennent, John, 155

Thermometers, 44, 49, 138

Thompson, Benjamin, Count Rumford, 156, 183-4, 203

Torricelli, 42, 44

Trades, histories of, 17-18, 25, 60-1

Trinity College, Cambridge, 47, 50, 167, 215

Uniformity, Act of, 165-6

Universities, 4, 9, 28-9, 87, 165-8, 180-1, 201-3; see also Education; Oxford University; Cambridge University

University College, 202; University of London, 202

Vanity of Dogmatizing, 57, 81

Vaughan, Lord, see Carbery, Earl of

Vesalius, Andreas, 41

Virtuosi: in 17th century, 27, 48, 50, 71, 92, 107; as collectors, 33-6; outstanding men, 43, 60, 88; first Fellows, 71, 75, 87-90; satires on, 87 et seq.; see also Amateurs

"Virtuoso," 92-4

Volta, Alessandro, 139

Voltaire, F. M. A. de, 125, 163

Wadham College, Oxford, 45 et seq., 73, 76, 88, 167

Waller, Richard, 100, 135, 150

Wallis, John, 2_, 37-8, 40, 45, 46-7, 54, 77

Ward, Seth, 29, 46, 48, 54, 55, 76, 97, 221

Warrington Academy, 166-7, 180

Watson, Richard, 180-1

Watt, James, 180

Wealth of Nations, The, 181

Weld, Charles R., 53, 122, 137

Whewell, William, 215-16

Wilkins, John: collector and virtuoso, 33-6, 49, 55; "invisible college," 37-9; Wadham College, 45 et seq.; Fellow, 50-1, 54; secretary, 65; scientific activities, 58, 78-80, 83, 85-6, 106-7, 199; death, 97, 199; legacy, 105-6, 227; influence on style and classification, 109-11; collected works, 126

William and Mary, 52, 120

Willis, Thomas, 84

Willughby, Francis, 55, 107, 108

Winthrop, John, governor of Connecticut, 55-6, 152, 156; John, grandson, 154

Winthrop, John, Harvard professor, 155

Wits, 57, 72 *et seq.*, 89-96, 114-15

Wolcot, John, *see* "Pindar, Peter"

Wollaston, William, 193, 205-6

Wood, Anthony, 86, 87

Wotton, William, 95-6

Wren, Christopher: genius, 42, 55, 72; friend of Sprat, 48; on Oldenburg, 66-7; Gresham professor, 50, 221; at Oxford, 167; Fellow, 54; researches, 76-7, 78, 84-6, 138; P.R.S., 99, 101, 149; architect, 77, 85-6, 111, 122; knighthood, 120-1; death, 126

Wren, Matthew, 54

Yale, Elihu, 153; College, 153, 159

York, James, Duke of, *see* James II

Young, Edward, 134